She was totally shaken by his kiss!

"Now, have you learned to respect my authority yet?" Alex asked as he released her. "After all, I am your boss."

Lauri thought of defying him yet again, but didn't dare incite another of those shattering kisses. "Yes," she said quietly.

"And you'll admit that there is an attraction between us, and go out with me willingly?"

"Yes," she agreed huskily.

Alex shook his head in a dazed fashion. "You never say what I expect you to say," he mused. "Maybe that's why I find you so intriguing. I don't think you'll bore me for a long time, Lauri."

But that day would come soon enough, Lauri realized bitterly. *That shouldn't stop me from enjoying this attraction here and now,* she tried telling herself....

CAROLE MORTIMER
is also the author of these

Harlequin Presents

Many of these titles are available at your local bookseller.

For a free catalogue listing all available Harlequin Romances
and Harlequin Presents, send your name and address to:

HARLEQUIN READER SERVICE
1440 South Priest Drive, Tempe, AZ 85281
Canadian address: Stratford, Ontario N5A 6W2

CAROLE MORTIMER

first love, last love

Harlequin Books

TORONTO • LONDON • LOS ANGELES • AMSTERDAM
SYDNEY • HAMBURG • PARIS • STOCKHOLM • ATHENS • TOKYO

Harlequin Presents edition published July 1981
ISBN 0-373-10443-X

Original hardcover edition published in 1981
by Mills & Boon Limited

CHAPTER ONE

"DON'T WAIT FOR ME TONIGHT," Jane advised. "Mr. Blair returns today, and I'm not sure what time I'll be able to get away. He has a habit of forgetting the time, especially when I have a date," she added ruefully.

Lauri looked up at the perfection of her young aunt, marveling at her cool beauty, her perfectly made-up face and smoothly styled black hair; she was stuck with a cap of red gold baby curls and freckles. She had tried all the suggested remedies she could find in magazines to get rid of the hated freckles, but still they remained, a fine sprinkling of them over her uptilted nose and just under her sparkling green eyes.

She was the odd one out in this family, her coloring at odds with both her young aunt and uncle. Jane and Steve, brother and sister, were both dark haired and dark eyed; Steve teased Lauri unmercifully about her "carrot top," but then he was always teasing her about something.

Lauri's parents had died eleven years ago when she was seven, leaving it up to Jane, then twenty-five, to care for her. Jane and Steve had lived with Lauri's parents, their brother, Robert, and his wife, Adelle, ever since the death of their own parents just after Lauri was born, and so it had seemed perfectly natural for the three of them to continue living together in this house.

Lauri had often wondered if caring for Steve and herself

was the reason Jane had never married, although Jane assured her it wasn't. And she never seemed to be short of male escorts, claiming it was her own choice to remain single.

"Do you have a date tonight?" she asked Jane now.

Her aunt shrugged. "Robin said he might call round. If it looks as if I'm going to be late I'll call him and tell him not to bother."

Lauri heaved an inward sigh of relief. She hadn't welcomed the idea of possibly having to keep Robin Harley entertained while they waited for Jane to come home. He was good-looking enough—extremely so—but he had a rather serious turn of conversation, often causing Steve to disappear behind a newspaper before his hysterical humor became obvious. Never taking anything seriously himself, Steve didn't appreciate anyone else who did.

"So Mr. Blair is coming back," Lauri mused. "Perhaps now I'll get to meet the man all the girls in the typing pool call the most exciting thing on two legs."

"And I thought that was me," Steve bemoaned across the breakfast table.

Lauri grinned at him. "I think you come way down the list."

"And I don't think you stand a chance of actually meeting Alexander Blair," he returned smugly.

"Why not?" she pouted. "I thought that with my aunt as his personal secretary, I stood a good chance."

"A good chance of what?" he teased.

She punched him on the arm, unrepentant at his exaggerated display of pain. "Meeting him," she said crossly. "And then you work in the sales department."

"As his top salesman. Well...almost," he amended at their teasing looks. "I was third in last year's figures," he defended.

"So you were," his sister smiled. "But then that hardly makes you the top salesman, does it?" She stood up, collecting her handbag. "If you want a lift, Lauri, you had better hurry. I daren't be late on Mr. Blair's first day back."

All three of them worked for Blair Computers, and although Jane started work half an hour before her, Lauri usually traveled in with her because Steve often went straight to see a client.

"I'm going into the office today," Steve informed them. "I have to catch up on my paperwork," he grimaced. With his natural good humor and easygoing ways he found his job as a salesman all too easy; it was the extensive paperwork that went with it that got him down. "So I'll give you a lift if you like, Lauri."

"When I can drive myself—"

"God help us," Steve muttered with a groan.

Lauri glared at him. "I'm not that bad. My instructor told me last week that he thinks I'm ready to take my test."

"What did you offer as a bribe?" he grinned.

"Nothing! You're always—"

"Children, children," Jane laughed at Lauri's furious expression. "Can you two never stop arguing?" she chided. "Well, I'm going to leave you to it. Don't forget the time."

It was a necessary warning; Steve and Lauri tended to forget everything else when they launched into one of their verbal onslaughts.

"See you later," they chorused together as Jane left.

"Now about your disparaging comments about my driving." Lauri turned on her young uncle as soon as they were alone. "How would you like to judge for yourself?" she challenged.

"Let you drive my car, you mean?"

"Why not? It's an old wreck, anyway, so it wouldn't matter even if I did hit a lamp post or something."

Steve looked outraged. "Gerty is not an old wreck!"

"Of course she is. I don't know why you can't drive a firm's car like all the other salesmen."

"Because I prefer Gerty to a Cortina."

"Fancy calling a car Gerty," Lauri scorned. "And as for it being a wreck—only your door opens, for a start, and then there's the rust, and then there's—"

"All right, all right," he cut in. "Gerty may not be the prettiest or most expensive car about, but she is reliable. The other chaps' cars are always breaking down."

"I suppose you were giving Gerty a holiday last week when you borrowed a car from the garage?" she taunted cheekily.

Steve flushed. "I was having the brakes looked at and you know it."

"Are you going to let me drive you in to work?" She stood up to remove the debris from breakfast. "Or are you too scared to entrust your precious car to me?" she goaded.

"Oh, you can drive." He threw her the car keys, pulling on his jacket. "I could do with a good laugh."

Lauri glared at him. "I'll show you! I'll make you eat your words."

"Well, come on then," he grinned. "We had better leave now; the speed you learner drivers go, it's likely to take twice as long to get there."

They clattered out of the house together. "We learner drivers take twice as long to get anywhere," she said explosively, "because we keep to the speed limit."

"You're a damned nuisance on the roads." Steve slid across the driving seat and into the passenger seat, the door next to him not having opened for months.

Lauri got in beside him, suddenly nervous for all of her bravado. She looked appealingly at her uncle. "You won't really laugh at me, will you?"

"No," he smiled. "But be careful. I know she looks a wreck, but she can travel."

Gerty was a low sports car, bright red in color where it hadn't rusted away, with humorous stickers on the doors and windows. After twelve years Gerty did indeed travel, and it took all Lauri's concentration to keep from going too fast.

"Mmm, not bad," Steve murmured as she turned into the firm's car park. "You only made one old lady drop her shopping and knocked some kid off his bike. Not bad at all."

"Ooh, I didn't!" She gave him a furious look.

That break in her concentration was her undoing. She had slowed right down to enter the car park, but when she returned her attention back to the front of her it was to find a two-tone brown and gold Rolls-Royce reversing into a space in front of her. Her foot slammed down on the brake—and nothing happened! Gerty kept right on moving, hitting the side of the Rolls with a thud.

"Why the hell didn't you brake?" Steve turned on her angrily.

"I did," she said indignantly. "I did!" she repeated at his skeptical look. "Nothing happened."

"That's damned obvious," he snapped. "Well, you've done it now." He nodded toward the other car as the furious driver climbed out from behind the wheel. "He isn't going to be very pleased about you denting his Rolls," he groaned.

"*He* isn't going to be very pleased?" Lauri exploded. "He had no right reversing up until I'd passed; he could see

me driving down this way. Anyway, I should think we've
done more damage to Gerty than to his car.''

"I doubt it will cost as much to repair," Steve muttered
with a groan.

"Well, we're certainly not paying for it." Her green eyes
sparkled as she thrust open the car door. "It's all *his* fault."
She glared at the back of the other driver as he inspected
where the two cars had made contact.

"Lauri!" Steve made a grab for her arm as she climbed
out of the car. "Lauri, for God's sake!" he cried after her.

She took no notice of him, marching purposefully over to
where the other driver was still bent over inspecting the
damage caused by the crash. Lauri brimmed over with re-
sentment. She supposed this man thought he owned the
place just because he had that flashy monster of a car. Well,
his obvious wealth didn't impress her!

"It was all your fault." She verbally attacked the broad
back and wide shoulders turned toward her. "You had no
right to be backing up like that when I could clearly be seen
driving in this direction."

Those forceful shoulders had stiffened at her first words
of rebuke, and now the dark head rose as the man slowly
turned to face her. Lauri was shocked into silence by startling blue eyes, sumptuously fringed with thick dark lashes,
a straight nose, a firm uncompromising mouth set in a disapproving line as the man made no effort to hide his
haughty disdain for her. His hair was jet black in color, and
styled away from his face to fall just below his collar, in-
clined to curl but obviously kept firmly in check.

The expensive cut of his suit spoke of extreme wealth,
and his arrogant manner indicated that he was a man accus-
tomed to authority. In his early thirties, Lauri would guess,
with a wealth of experience to go with those years.

"So it was my fault, was it?" The icy contempt in his voice made Lauri cringe. "Then how do you account for the fact that *your* car is smashed into the side of mine?"

Her face was bright red with temper, her freckles more noticeable. "I've already told you. You—"

"Lauri, will you be quiet!" Steve swung her round, his dark eyes flashing a warning. "Behave yourself," he hissed.

"I was only—"

"Lauri!" he repeated tautly. He turned to the other man. "I'm very sorry about this—"

"Sorry!" his niece cut in. "We're not sorry at all. And we aren't paying for it, either. He was—"

"Lauri!" Steve's fingers bit painfully into her arm as he pulled her roughly against his side. "Just shut up!"

"But he— Ouch!" she cried out as he increased the pressure of his fingers. "That hurt," she complained.

"It was meant to. Just behave yourself." Again he turned to the other man. "I hope there isn't too much damage to your car, sir."

"Sir...?" Lauri's mouth fell open as she stared at the owner of the Rolls. "Steve, is he...?"

"Yes!" he hissed down at her.

"Oh, my God!" she gulped, gazing fearfully at the man she now knew to be Alexander Blair. No wonder he looked as if he owned the place—he did! And she had just accused him of negligent driving, had been thoroughly rude to him, in fact. And he didn't look as if he had a very forgiving nature.

Alexander Blair looked at Steve with steady blue eyes. "You know who I am?"

"Yes, Mr. Blair. I, er, I work for you," he admitted reluctantly.

"Really?" Dark eyebrows rose. "And your girl friend?"

"I'm not—"

"Lauri works for you, too," Steve cut in on her indignant denial. "I really am sorry about your car, Mr. Blair. If you send the bill to me, Steve Prescott, Sales Department, I'll gladly pay it."

"Very well." Their employer nodded abruptly. "And in future I would refrain from letting your girl friend get behind the wheel of your car. I've invariably found that women don't have the concentration for it. I'm sure—Lauri, was it—I'm sure she had her mind on other things, possibly the clothes she would be wearing for your date tonight," he derided.

She gasped. "Why, you—"

"And hot-headed female drivers are the worst of the lot," he added dryly.

Steve grinned. "I only let her drive me in today so that she could prove what a good driver she is."

The first glimmer of humor lightened those harsh features as Alexander Blair looked pointedly at the touching vehicles. "I would say she has proven the opposite," he drawled mockingly.

Lauri's temper rose at the condescending look in those startling blue eyes. "I didn't prove anything—"

"I couldn't agree more," he cut in scathingly.

"I was going to say anything of the sort," she snapped, her mouth tight, caution thrown to the winds. "I still maintain that it was your fault. You—"

"Get in the car." Steve gave her a threatening glare. "Go on, get in," he ordered. "The passenger side. I'll just sort matters out with Mr. Blair."

"But, Steve—"

"For once in your unruly life will you do as you're told!"

Lauri flinched at the fury in her uncle's voice, his anger

unusual and so all the more effective. "Yes, Steve." She bowed her head, studiously avoiding the taunting humor Alexander Blair made no effort to hide. She threw her head back challengingly, walking slowly round to the side of the car that had recently held Steve. She clambered over the low side, not willing to go back round to the door that actually opened.

She glowered at the two men as they talked together, her arms folded mutinously across her chest. Arrogant, condescending, mocking...! How on earth could he be thought the sexiest thing on two legs! She thought he was hateful— very handsome, but hateful nonetheless.

Steve grinned at her as he got back into the sports car, nodding to the other man as he completed the task of reversing the Rolls back into his reserved parking space. The car had a personalized number plate, AB 1, and maybe if Lauri had been given the chance to see this she might have made the connection between her employer and the man who had so haughtily told her the accident was her fault. Her fault indeed! He just hadn't been looking where he—

"Calm down, firebrand," Steve teased. "You really will have to learn to control that temper of yours, infant. You simply don't talk to men of Alexander Blair's caliber like that, especially as our livelihood depends on him. He could have turned nasty and sacked us, you know."

"Just for hitting his stupid car?" she scoffed. "He couldn't get away with that. It would be unfair dismissal."

"When you ranted and raved at him like a mad thing?" His eyebrows rose. "I think he would have sufficient reason for getting rid of you." He parked the car before helping Lauri out as she slid along the seat. "He still could, come to think of it."

"He doesn't know who I am," she said smugly. "Only

that I'm your girl friend." She gave him a scathing look. "As if I could fancy *you*!" she dismissed disgustedly. "Why didn't you tell him I'm your niece? At least then he wouldn't have reason to question my taste in men."

"You're a cheeky, outspoken little devil, and if you aren't careful someone is going to take you down a peg or two." He ushered her through the double glass doors that were the entrance to Blair Computers.

"Not you?" she scorned.

He sighed. "Not me. I don't have the stamina. It's going to take a strong man to pin you down."

"No man will ever do that," she vowed vehemently. "I intend staying free of those sort of entanglements."

The lift stopped, the doors opened. Steve pushed her out. "Off you go, infant. And try not to fall foul of our provider again." He grimaced. "I just hope the insurance people will cough up; I certainly can't pay for the repairs to a Rolls out of my own pocket. You were right about those brakes," he added thoughtfully. "They aren't catching properly."

Lauri frowned. "Nevertheless, I was the one who crashed. You can't take the blame."

"It's my responsibility. And I don't want anyone probing into this too deeply; don't forget we didn't have L-plates up. Thank God Blair didn't realize you're still a learner; he would probably have ripped me to pieces."

Lauri shook her head. "I don't think he's the physical sort."

Steve grinned. "That isn't what I heard," he said suggestively.

"You're disgusting!" she had time to shout before the lift doors closed. Trust him to take her words the wrong way!

She could imagine that Alexander Blair could be very

physical, given a beautiful woman in the right setting. It made her body tingle and her skin color a delicate pink at the thought of that handsome specimen of a man in such an intimate situation. She had no doubt he would be a good lover; he didn't keep his many women just because he was rich.

She had been hearing about Alexander Blair's life, both business and private, for the last three years, ever since Jane had become his personal secretary, in fact. He was an astute and ruthless businessman, that much she had gathered from the little Jane was prepared to tell, her aunt's loyalty all to her boss's privacy, despite Lauri's interested questioning. His private life was a lot easier to hear about; often in the gossip columns, Alexander Blair seemed to change his women at regular intervals, each one seeming to last an average of two to three months. Until he tired of them, no doubt. Her brief meeting with him this morning had shown her that he was a man people rarely said no to.

She wondered what he would look like when he wasn't furiously angry or being tauntingly sarcastic. Very handsome, with a somehow earthy quality, a hint of sensuality in the fullness of his bottom lip and the very deep blue of his eyes. Yes, there was no doubt that if he set out to be charming, Alexander Blair could charm anyone.

Except her! She wouldn't ever be charmed by that insufferable—

"Hey, sleepyhead," a voice broke into her thoughts. "I've spoken to you twice and you haven't heard a word I've said."

Lauri looked ruefully at Diane, one of her workmates in the typing pool. They had apparently been sharing the same mirror for the last five minutes or so as they tidied themselves before the start of the day, although Lauri had been unaware of it, her attention solely on Alexander Blair. Drat the man!

"Did you ask your aunt about Mr. Blair?" Diane was obviously repeating the question, her tone patient.

Lauri frowned at the mention of the man she had just discovered she disliked intensely. "Ask her what?"

Her friend sighed. "Whether he's coming back today. The place has been dead without him this last month."

As far as Lauri was concerned it could have remained dead; she could certainly have done without this morning's incident. "He's back," she told Diane firmly.

Her blue eyes widened. "He is?"

"Mmm. I just—I saw him in the car park just now." She didn't want to tell anyone she had just made a nasty dent in his beautiful car. She would never live down such notoriety. And Jane would be furious.

"How does he look?" Diane asked eagerly as they walked down the corridor to their office.

"Tanned," Lauri grimaced.

"Well, of course he's tanned; he's been in America the last four weeks. What I meant is, is he still as good-looking as ever, the sexy devil?"

"I suppose so. And I thought he went to America to work, not to get himself a suntan," she added bitchily.

Diane gave her a teasing look. "Don't tell me I've actually found someone who doesn't think our boss is the dishiest male ever."

"You've found her—me," Lauri confirmed.

The other girl's eyes widened. "Didn't you think he was gorgeous?" she gasped.

"He was all right," she admitted grudgingly.

"All right!" Diane sounded scandalized. "My God,

girls," she addressed the other typists in the room. "Meet someone who's immune to the sexy Alexander."

"You can't be!"

"Surely not, Lauri!"

"I think he's lovely."

"His eyes are just mesmerizing," someone else sighed.

Lauri let the outrageous comments pass over her, unaffected by her colleagues' obvious disbelief at her disinterest. "I suppose his eyes are quite fascinating," she said with remembered attraction. Deep blue eyes they had been, fringed by long dark lashes. Yes, they could be called mesmerizing, very mesmerizing, if they weren't looking at you as if you were a particularly obnoxious insect that had wandered into his vicinity. How Jane could work in such close contact with him she just couldn't imagine, although Jane had always maintained he was a fair man to work for.

"Big of you to admit it," Jeannie teased.

Lauri took the cover off her typewriter. "You can't deny the truth. But looks aren't everything."

"Don't tell me looks don't enter into your dating Daryl, because I just won't believe it." Diane sat at the adjoining desk. "A big, blond, muscular Canadian," she teased.

Lauri blushed. "He's intelligent, too," she defended the boy she had been dating the last couple of weeks, a Canadian of twenty who did temporary work to subsidize his traveling around the world. At the moment he was working in the accounts department here.

"Oh, I'm glad about that," her friend laughed. "Don't get me wrong; I think he's really nice, very good-looking, but you must have noticed those looks before you ever found out what a nice person he is."

"Mmm...I suppose so. But Alexander Blair doesn't appear to me to be a nice person." Far from it!

"That's not what his girl friends think."

"Doesn't the fact that it's girls, in the plural, tell you anything?"

Diane laughed. "Oh, yes, it tells me something."

"I didn't mean that!" Lauri said impatiently.

"I did," Diane laughed again.

"I'm going to do some work," Lauri said crossly. "Before Carly starts chucking her weight about," she added mischievously.

"I heard that," called her supervisor, a young girl of twenty who ruled by friendly teamwork rather than by issuing orders.

Lauri grinned before bending over her work, the subject of her not liking Alexander Blair forgotten for the moment—at least by the other girls it was. She was still seething at his high-handedness.

She met Daryl for lunch as usual, and they went to the local Wimpy bar, Lauri biting hungrily into her delicious hamburger. "Mmm, I needed that." She sat back with a grin. "Is there something wrong with yours?" She noticed he didn't appear to be enjoying it.

"It's all right." His Canadian accent was very noticeable. "I'm just not hungry." He pushed his plate away.

Lauri frowned, her green eyes troubled. "What is it, Daryl? What's wrong?"

"You know what's wrong," he told her moodily. "Although you don't seem to give a damn. I go to Ireland at the end of the week and—"

"And I'm not going with you," she said patiently. "I've told you before, I don't want to go."

"But if you don't come with me, I won't see you again."

"You don't have to leave, Daryl," she pointed out reasonably. "You can always stay here."

He sighed. "My job at Blair's finishes on Friday. Besides, I've already got my fare to Ireland booked; it was booked long before I even met you."

"I'm not going with you, Daryl, so you might as well stop sulking and eat your lunch."

His hand moved to caress hers as it lay on her denim-clad thigh. "I can't think of food when I'm going to be parted from you at the end of the week."

"Don't be silly," she laughed lightly. "I've only known you a couple of weeks; we hardly know one another well enough to—to—"

"I'm not asking for more than a traveling companion," he persisted. "We would have separate accommodations."

"At the beginning," she said knowingly. "I'm not that naive, Daryl. How long do you think it would be before you suggested we save the expense of the second room?"

His tanned golden skin colored a ruddy hue, and he looked slightly sheepish. "I never thought of you as a prude."

"Oh, not that!" she laughed again. "You won't get round me by issuing that sort of challenge. I'm not a prude, but neither am I a sleep-around. We've had a good couple of weeks, had fun together; let's leave it at that, hmm?"

"I don't want to." His hand tightened on hers. "Come with me, Lauri. Please!"

She sighed. "I told you, no." She pulled her hand out of his. "My aunt would never agree, anyway," she added, as if that ended the matter. She would never go against Jane, loving and respecting her too much to hurt her.

Daryl scowled. "She acts more like your mother than your aunt."

Daryl and Jane had only met once, one evening when Daryl had returned Lauri home rather late, and her aunt had shown her displeasure with the lateness of the hour. They had taken an instant dislike to each other, and although Jane never tried to influence her in her choice of friends, Lauri had been conscious of her aunt's disapproval of Daryl.

"In a way she is; she's brought me up since I was seven," Lauri bristled angrily on behalf of her aunt. "And we were late that night. She had a right to be cross with us."

"It was a Saturday, Lauri. You didn't have to go to work in the morning. And we had been to a party."

"It was three o'clock in the morning!"

He smiled. "Some of the parties I go to back home go on until morning."

"They do here, too, and I've been to a couple of them, but not without informing Jane first."

"She isn't your keeper!" he said resentfully.

Lauri sighed. "I'm not going to argue with you, Daryl, not at this late date in our friendship. We'll just have to agree to differ about the loyalty and respect I owe my aunt."

"We weren't talking about respect. I was just—"

"Let's forget it, Daryl! Please. I'm not going to Ireland or anywhere else with you, and it's my decision. Now, where are you taking me tonight?"

"Are you sure you still want to go anywhere with me?" he said moodily.

"Don't be a bad loser," she chided, aware that his usual good humor and bland good looks had made him some easy conquests on his travels. She just didn't intend being one of them. "Now eat your food; we have to be back in a few minutes."

"I don't want it." He obviously still hadn't got over his sulk.

"Moody," she teased. "Hey, I know—we could go to the cinema this evening. There's a good film on at the Odeon."

"If you want to." They moved to pay their bill before going outside.

She looked up at him. "Don't you want to know what the film is?"

"Not particularly."

"Now, look," she snapped. "We can finish this right now if you're going to continue behaving childishly. And it *is* childish to sulk just because you can't have your own way."

"You would like Ireland; I know you would."

"I'm sure I would," she agreed. "But I'm still not going. I have no desire to travel. Maybe one day I will have, but not right now."

"I'm going to miss you."

She grinned. "I'll bet—for the first five minutes. Just think of all those Irish colleens, and I'm sure you'll soon cheer up."

A reluctant smile lightened his features. "Aren't you ever serious?"

"Not if I can help it," she admitted. "Steve is the same. We have some lovely arguments."

"But not with Jane."

"No one argues with Jane. She's always cool and calm. Perhaps that's why she gets on with our bossy Mr. Blair," she mused. "She would just soothe his temper away."

"Bossy? Temper?" Daryl frowned. "You speak like one who knows, and yet I thought your aunt never discussed him with you."

"He's back, you know."

"Oh, I know. The whole building has been buzzing with it all morning. But as far as I know he hasn't stepped foot outside his office. I wouldn't recognize him if I saw him."

Neither had she! "He was away when we both started with the firm," she evaded.

"Then how do you know he's bossy and has a temper?"

She shrugged. "It stands to reason."

"I don't see why."

"Of course it does. The man's used to his own way—look at all the women he has—and he's bound to be bossy being in such a position of authority."

He shook his head. "It doesn't follow."

"All right, so it doesn't follow," she snapped impatiently, feeling as if she had done nothing but talk about Alexander Blair all day. "Are we going to the cinema this evening or not?" she changed the subject.

"We are." He opened the lift doors for her, waiting until it began moving before turning to her.

Lauri knew of his intention to kiss her as soon as his arm went about her shoulders, and she lifted her head invitingly. She had always found his kisses pleasant, never allowing him to do any more than kiss her, and she found this lengthy caress as pleasurable as usual.

"If you'll excuse me?" a glacial voice remarked.

Without them being aware of it, the lift had come to a halt at Daryl's floor, and a man stood outside waiting to get in. Lauri's heart sank as she recognized Alexander Blair. And it was obvious he recognized her, too, his gaze passing scathingly over her as she still stood in the circle of Daryl's arms.

"Sorry," Daryl grinned at the older man. "Just kissing my girl goodbye until tonight."

Dark eyebrows rose. "*Your* girl?" Alexander Blair inquired coolly.

Lauri struggled out of Daryl's arms, straightening her slim-fitting sweater where it had ridden up to reveal her midriff, and pushing a hurried hand through her rumpled red gold curls. This was terrible! And poor Daryl could have no idea of who their audience had been.

Daryl grinned. "Just for the rest of this week," he confided.

"I see. And then you, er, part company?" Alexander Blair was obviously weighing up this information, drawing his own conclusions about the closeness of the relationship.

"Yeah," Daryl laughed. "I guess we do. The lady refuses to travel around the world with me."

"I would think the... lady—" he drawled the word as if he hardly thought the description fitted Lauri "—I would think she's having too much fun where she is."

"You're probably right," Daryl acknowledged. He bent to kiss her briefly on the lips. "I'd better get back to work. Old Crowther's prowling about timing everything we do with the boss back in town. See you later, sweetheart," he grinned, his good humor back in evidence. "See you," he nodded to Alexander Blair.

"No doubt," the other man agreed softly.

Lauri hardly dared breathe once the lift doors had closed behind Daryl's departing figure. This just wasn't her day! First of all she hit Alexander Blair's Rolls-Royce, and now he had caught her kissing one of her fellow workers in the lift.

"That was quite an exhibition," he remarked scornfully.

Her cheeks flamed at his insulting tone. "It wasn't meant to be a peepshow," she snapped, glaring up at him as he towered over her, his six feet in height reducing her to his shoulder height.

"I don't recall peeping," he mocked.

"No," she agreed angrily. "You had a damned good look, didn't you?"

"I could hardly do anything else," he said coldly. "And let me tell you that I am unaccustomed to summoning the lift and finding two of my employees in a passionate clinch when the doors open."

"It wasn't a *passionate* clinch," she denied heatedly, her green eyes flashing.

"No?"

"No!"

"Then what would you call a passionate clinch?" he asked softly.

Lauri shrugged. "I don't know. But that wasn't one."

"Perhaps not," he said calmly. "How would you gauge this?"

Before she had had time to do more than gasp, his arms were about her and his dark head swooped as his lips claimed hers in what was definitely a passionate clinch. His mouth moved persuasively against hers, parting her lips with the sensuous tip of his tongue, kissing her more intimately than anyone else had ever done, his hands molding her to the lean length of his body.

Lauri had never experienced anything like it before, feeling as if the world were spinning, and that all that mattered was that he should go on kissing her. That *Alexander Blair* should go on kissing her.

Suddenly she was free, Alexander Blair looking for all the world as if that devastating kiss had never taken place, totally in command in the light gray suit and snowy white silk shirt that both looked as if they had been tailored onto him. His impeccable appearance made her own denims and jumper all the more conspicuous.

"Well?" he taunted.

"Well...?" she repeated dazedly. "Oh," she nodded. "Er, yes."

"Yes—what?"

"Just yes," she said breathlessly.

He smiled, but it wasn't a pleasant smile. "Do you always give in on such short acquaintance? If so, I'm not surprised at your popularity with my male employees."

His scorn shocked her out of the sensual enchantment she seemed to have fallen into. "I wasn't saying yes to *that!*" she denied hotly. "I was just saying that it—that was a passionate embrace. And given by an expert, I have no doubt."

"Insults, Lauri?"

"You deserve them. How dare you kiss me?"

He gave a throaty laugh. "I dare. Your name," he said thoughtfully. "It isn't really Lauri?"

She frowned. "No. Lauren."

"Lauren," he savored it. "Mmm, I like it."

What did she care what he liked! "I've always been called Lauri," she said defensively.

He nodded. "That accounts for it."

Long after she was back at her desk the question still plagued her. "Accounted" for what?

CHAPTER TWO

STEVE SAT AT THE TABLE watching Lauri as she prepared their evening meal. "Had a good day?" he taunted, leaning forward on his elbows.

"Fantastic!" she drawled sarcastically. "Really great. I crashed my uncle's car into my boss's Rolls this morning, had an argument with my boyfriend at lunchtime because I refused to go on his travels with him, and then—"

"Yes?" Steve prompted curiously. "And then?"

Lauri's cheeks were bright red. "And then the bus was fifteen minutes late tonight." She had no intention of telling anyone about that unexpected kiss Alexander Blair had given her. After all, the kiss had been given as an insult, and although she may have reacted to it, the insult had still gone home.

"Oh," he nodded. "I see. So Daryl's been trying to persuade you to take off with him, has he. I'm glad you've decided not to go with him."

"I thought you liked him." She placed a mug of tea in front of him.

"I do, he's a great chap; I just don't fancy him as a nephew-in-law."

Lauri laughed, going back to her cooking. "I don't think Daryl had marriage in mind."

"Really? Then I wouldn't have let you go, anyway."

"*You* wouldn't?" She turned from checking the vegetables. "You wouldn't have any say in it if I had wanted to go. I make my own mind up about things like that."

Steve shook his head. "Not this time. You're still a kid, Lauri—only seventeen—much too young to make those sort of decisions."

"And I suppose an old-timer like you knows all about these things?" They had always found the eight years difference between them faintly amusing; they were more like brother and sister than uncle and niece.

"That's right." He stood up to ruffle her red gold curls into disorder, tapping her lightly on the end of her freckled snub nose. "You're just a baby."

She grinned. "I'm old enough to have crashed your car for you."

He sobered. "So you are. I'm still waiting for Blair to get back to me on that."

"Bit early, isn't it?"

Steve shrugged. "I can't see him driving around in a dented car for long."

Neither could she. It didn't fit in with his impeccable appearance. Even after he had kissed her he had remained unruffled. But she didn't want to think of that kiss—or her reaction to it!

"Lauri?"

"Mmm? Sorry." She snapped out of her daze at Steve's puzzled look. "It's just been one of those days."

"Don't I know it," he groaned. "Poor old Gerty will never be the same. The front of her looks—"

"Shush!" she hurriedly interrupted him. "I hear Jane's key in the door," she explained at his indignant look. "And I don't want her to know about the accident."

He grimaced. "If she's seen my car she'll already know about it; there's brown paint mixed up with the red."

Lauri groaned. "You didn't leave it parked outside?"

"Of course I did. I'm going out later."

"Oh, God! I'll just have to hope Jane isn't very observant. Can you imagine what she would say if she knew I'd smashed into her boss's car?"

"I can." He grinned. "And he's our boss, too," he reminded.

How could she forget it! "At least we don't work for him directly. If he knew I was Jane's niece...!"

"Mmm, I see your point. Okay, I'll keep quiet unless directly asked."

"Now is that likely? There's no reason why Jane should make the connection— Hello, Jane." She turned to greet her young aunt. "Sit down, love," she encouraged on seeing her tired face. "You look worn out."

Jane did as she suggested, literally collapsing into the chair. "I look worn out because I am worn out. Thanks, Lauri." She took the proffered cup of tea, sipping gratefully. "Mr. Blair was an absolute swine this morning."

"Perhaps his business trip to the States didn't work out as he wanted it to." Lauri's look was almost hopeful that that had been the reason.

"Oh, it wasn't that—that went fine," Jane instantly dismissed, slipping off her shoes to flex her tired feet. "No, it was something else that upset him."

"Oh?" Lauri asked innocently.

"Mmm." Jane put her head back, closing her eyes. "Some idiot smashed into his car this morning."

"Some idiot!" Lauri echoed indignantly.

"Is that what he said?" chuckled Steve.

"Mmm," Jane murmured wearily. "God, he's been impossible to work for all day. He had just started to get over it by lunchtime, but when he came back he was in an even worse mood."

And didn't Lauri know it! She may have been the cause of his first anger, but she had been made to bear the brunt of his lunchtime upset. Her mouth still tingled from that onslaught. What on earth would Jane and Steve say if they knew about it? She shuddered to think—especially cool, calm Jane, who always kept men at a distance, including Robin Harley.

"Maybe his ladylove doesn't like lunchtime sessions," Steve joked.

His sister gave him a reproving look. "I don't appreciate those sorts of comments about Mr. Blair. He had a business appointment. Anyway, Miss Mears is out of town."

"*Connie* Mears?" Lauri gasped. "The model?" A vision of a tall leggy blonde instantly sprang to mind.

"Is there another one?" Steve quipped.

Lauri glared at him. "There could be."

He shook his head. "Not if Alexander Blair is dating her."

"I'm sure he isn't the type to be faithful to one woman," Lauri said bitchily. "Perhaps some other female turned him down at lunchtime." Which would account for his attack on her!

"Lauri!" Jane reprimanded. "I won't have you talking like that, even if Steve chooses to."

"Don't be such a nag, Jane. Personally, I don't think Mr. High-and-mighty Blair merits your unwavering loyalty to him. So far I've found him to be simply awful. He's overbearing, impossible—"

"So far?" Jane frowned. "You've *met* Mr. Blair?"

Too late she realized her mistake. "Well, er, no, not exactly. He— Oh, goodness, look at the gravy!" She rushed to the cooker, pulling the saucepan off the heat to stop it from boiling all over the sparkling white top. "Dinner is ready; let's eat before it spoils." She clutched thankfully onto this excuse to change the subject. "Go and have a quick wash, Jane, while I serve the food."

"That was a narrow escape," Steve said once they were alone. "If you aren't careful, Lauri, that temper of yours is going to be what lands you in trouble. I won't mention who Blair thinks is an idiot, but I think you just might let that out yourself if you aren't a little more careful of what you say."

Lauri took his advice and remained silent when her aunt came back, listening to their conversation but adding little herself. Jane would be furious if she found out her niece had been driving the car that had so upset their employer, and Jane had quite a biting tongue if she became angry.

They had finished their main course and were just starting on the apple crumble and custard they had for dessert when Steven flashed Lauri a sly look. He feigned a look of innocence. "Our little niece was propositioned today," he told his sister casually.

Lauri gasped, biting back her fiery retort. What could he possibly know of that kiss in the lift?

"Yes," he continued softly. "Some Lothario wanted to whisk her off round the world with him."

She almost sighed her relief out loud. "Daryl isn't a Lothario," she defended, perhaps more heatedly than normal because she had thought Steve meant Alexander Blair. "He's a very nice boy."

"Then why did you refuse to go with him?" Steve taunted.

Her green eyes flashed. "Because—because I've only just started my new job," she desperately made up an excuse.

He laughed. "And you enjoy being a typist so much that it wins hands down over traveling the world."

"Anyone would think you wanted me to go," Lauri snapped.

"Will you two stop arguing!" Jane put her hands up to her temples. "I have a splitting headache and all you two can do is bicker all the time." She gave Lauri a sharp look. "When did Daryl ask you to go away with him?" she demanded to know.

"Oh, weeks ago," she dismissed. "I told him I thought it was a ridiculous idea."

"But he asked you again today?"

Lauri grinned. "He's a trier."

"As long as he doesn't succeed," Steve quipped.

"Steven!" Jane rounded on him. "It isn't something to joke about."

He sobered. "I couldn't agree more. I told her we wouldn't have let her go even if she had decided to go with him."

"And I told you that *I* make those sort of decisions for myself." Lauri stood up, angrily removing the empty plates. "Just because we all live here together doesn't mean you can push me around. You act more like my parents than my aunt and uncle. I'm fed up with it all the time. Why can't you both mind—"

"Lauri!" Steve cut in warningly. "Can't you see Jane's had enough?"

Her aunt was in fact very pale, and she instantly felt contrite. "Go and lay down for a while." She moved to her aunt's side. "It might ease your headache."

"Yes," Jane agreed faintly. "I—I think I'll do that."

Lauri helped her to her feet. "I'll cancel your date with Robin, shall I? I think you might be better for an early night."

"I— Yes, maybe that would be best." For once the fight seemed to have gone out of Jane, dear dependable Jane who had brought Steve and Lauri up single-handedly since the double tragedy of first her own parents' death and then the death of her brother and his wife. "But I'll call Robin and explain," she added.

"And you aren't going to work tomorrow if you aren't feeling any better," Lauri told her sternly. "You can let that bully—you can let Mr. Blair find someone else to use as a punch bag." She cursed herself for once again letting her feelings toward that man run away with her.

Jane gave a wan smile. "I wouldn't exactly say he went that far."

"He must have been pretty nasty to have reduced you to this state. Now come on, bed."

Steve had already left when she came back from settling Jane down, and so she set about wiping the crockery he had thoughtfully washed before going out. She was worried about Jane; it wasn't like her to feel ill, and the fact that Alexander Blair had been indirectly responsible only made Lauri dislike him all the more. Bad-tempered, arrogant swine! Jane must be mad to work for him.

Lauri hadn't known he was dating Connie Mears—that little bit of gossip hadn't reached the lower ranks yet. Connie Mears and Alexander Blair; however did the poor girl put up with his arrogance? If he kissed the other woman as he had her today, then she knew the answer to that. Even while the kiss had not been given to evoke pleasure, she had been aware of the mastery and experience behind the caress, so much experience that she had responded in spite of herself.

She blushed in shame at the memory of her reaction. And what made it worse was the fact that Alexander Blair had known of her response, had even taunted her about it. He had made her shiver with pleasure when he had lingered over the use of her full name, almost making a caress of it.

Well, she wouldn't think about him anymore! Daryl was more in her league, and he would be arriving in a minute.

IT DIDN'T SEEM to be her week. Yesterday had been disastrous, not least being her argument with Daryl in the evening. He had gone on and on about her going to Ireland with him until in the end she had lost her temper with him and demanded to be taken home.

And now she had stupidly left her purse in Jane's handbag. She never carried a handbag herself, and her tight denims didn't allow for the bulge of a purse. She usually pushed some money loosely into one of her pockets. But she had been late this morning, accepting Jane's offer of a lift at the last minute—Jane seemed to have recovered from her tiredness completely—and had just grabbed her purse and ran. And now she had left it, and consequently her money, in Jane's bag.

Thank God she had realized more or less straight away; it was still only a quarter to nine, she had plenty of time to get to the top floor, collect her purse and get back down again before nine o'clock.

It seemed unusually quiet up here, not at all like the rush and bustle that preceded the start of the day on the lower floors. Her moccasin-clad feet sank into the luxurious green carpet. The whole decor up here was complete luxury.

She had no idea which door led to Jane's office, and so she had to walk along inspecting all of the nameplates. She had just about given up hope of finding the right one when a door opened just up the corridor from her and she could hear the murmur of male voices. Maybe she could ask the way to Jane's office; after all, she wasn't doing anything wrong, and the minutes to nine o'clock were fast ticking away.

A man came out of the office and shut the door after him, bending over the papers he held in his hand. His head may be bent and his face partly hidden, but Lauri would recognize that thick dark hair, wide expanse of shoulders in the tailored cream suit and contrasting brown shirt anywhere. Alexander Blair!

As if becoming aware of someone watching him, he slowly raised his head, deep blue eyes widening with recognition. "You!" he rasped, reaching her side in two long strides. He grasped her arm. "What are you doing up here?"

"I—"

"Lost your way?" he taunted.

"Certainly not!" Her face flushed angrily. "Actually, I— I was looking for you." Good heavens, what had she said now? But she could hardly tell him the truth, not when she didn't want him to know the connection between his secretary and herself.

His eyebrows rose. "For me?"

"Er—yes." Now what did she say!

"Well?" His stance was challenging. "Now you've found me."

"Yes," she acknowledged huskily.

"So?" His eyes were narrowed. "What can I do for you?"

What *could* he do? She thought rapidly. "It's what I can do for you," she said breathlessly.

"Really?" his voice taunted, a humorless smile to his lips. "Isn't it a little early in the day to be making those sort of suggestions?"

Her face flushed fiery red at his gibe. "I didn't mean it like that and you know it!" she snapped.

"Do I? And why should I know that? You seem to have two boyfriends that I know of, possibly more, and I made the

mistake of kissing you yesterday. Maybe you've come to continue where we left off."

"No, I haven't! And I don't have two boyfriends! As for
that kiss, you can't think it any more a mistake than I do."

"That wasn't the impression you gave yesterday," he
drawled.

"Why, you arrogant— How dare you!" Her hands
clenched at her sides. "You forced me to kiss you back,"
she accused. "I didn't have any choice in the matter."

"A lady always has a choice," he taunted. "Although
you could hardly be classed as a lady, not even a *young* lady—
more like a girl, really. How old are you?"

She was so startled by the question she replied instantly.
"Eighteen—nearly nineteen," she added defensively.

His eyes narrowed. "How nearly?"

"Nearly!" she repeated resentfully.

"Which means you've only just turned eighteen." He
watched the guilty color enter her cheeks. "I thought so.
Aren't you a little young to be doing this sort of thing?"

Lauri frowned. "What sort of thing?"

"Chasing men, especially one almost twice your age."

"I am not chasing— *Are* you really that old?" she asked
insultingly.

His mouth tightened. "Or you're that young; it depends
which way you look at it."

"That makes you two years younger than my aunt," she
said thoughtfully.

"Really?" He looked down impatiently at his wristwatch,
a plain gold affair, more indicative of his wealth than a
flashy one would have been. People who were as rich as he
never needed to flaunt it—it was just there in their every
movement, every word. "Now what did you want to see me
about?"

"Your car," she feverishly grasped for something to say. "I, er, I wanted to know if you had had anything done about it yet," she explained with a certain amount of triumph, pleased with herself for thinking of something so quickly.

"As it happens I have. But I thought your boyfriend was dealing with that?"

"He isn't my boyfriend!" she said crossly. "He—he's a friend, that's all."

"And do all your boyfriends later become just friends?"

She drew an angry breath. "He's always been just a friend."

"That takes care of him," he remarked thoughtfully. "And the other boyfriend departs at the end of the week. Would that be Saturday?"

"Morning," she nodded. "But—"

"Then that leaves you free to have dinner with me Saturday evening."

Her eyes became huge in her surprise and disbelief. "I—I beg your pardon? What did you say?"

"Isn't dinner suitable? Or are you one of these females that makes do with a cracker and an apple?"

"I've always had a healthy appetite. But—"

"Then dinner it is." He gave another glance at his watch. "I have to get to a meeting now, so if you'll just tell me where you live I can be on my way."

Lauri shook her head dazedly, searching his arrogant features for some sign of mockery. The mouth looked impatient, the eyes questioning, but as far as she could see there was no mockery there. "Who says I want to have dinner with you?" she demanded, annoyed with his assumption in thinking she would agree.

He sighed. "Don't you?"

"Not particularly. Just because your girl friend is out of town doesn't mean I'm willing to—"

"It would appear you aren't *willing* to do anything without an argument," he said tersely. "I made the suggestion in the hope that we might come to some agreement over the payment for the damage to my car." He shrugged. "But if you would rather it went through the insurance agents, that's just fine by me. Of course, you may have a little difficulty explaining to the police what you were doing driving without L-plates, but then that's your choice."

Lauri's mouth gaped open. "You know?" she asked in a whisper.

"That you're a learner? If I didn't before I do now. You just confirmed my suspicions."

"Why, you— That wasn't fair. You tricked me!"

"Not really," he said calmly. "It was a natural assumption to make. Your driving leaves a lot to be desired, and by your own admission you're only just eighteen." He eyed her mockingly. "So it would be very doubtful you had already taken a driving test, not with the way our system works. I took a shot in the dark and it paid off. Your friend is a braver man than I to allow you to drive his car."

She blushed at the sarcasm in his voice. "I don't suppose you ever let anyone drive you."

"Never. Not even the girl friend you say is out of town. Tell me," he taunted. "Who is she?"

"You must know who she is! I wish you would stop treating me like an idiot." She glared angrily as she realized that was exactly what he had called her to Jane. "You may think that's what I am, but that doesn't mean you have to treat me like one. Everyone knows you're seeing Connie Mears." A slight exaggeration here, but she felt she could be forgiven it.

"Then 'everyone' is wrong. Do the gossips have nothing better to do than make up stories to color their day?"

No doubt he considered her to be one of the gossips! "I got my information from a reliable source," she said defensively.

"Then it's a little dated," he returned coldly. "Connie and I finished weeks ago."

"Oh. I—I didn't know that."

He gave her a long slow appraisal, making her blush from head to toe at the undisguised insolence in those deep blue eyes. "There's no reason why you should know. And I wouldn't consider you a suitable replacement in any case. I was hardly asking you for a date, Lauren—just trying to work this thing out like two reasonable adul—people," he amended tauntingly.

"I am an adult!"

"You don't act like one. Look, I couldn't give a damn whether this goes through the police or not; it's completely up to you."

He obviously felt he had wasted enough time on her for one day. But Lauri couldn't let him go like this. "Do the police have to be involved?" She despised herself for that almost pleading quality in her voice.

"I told you that is up to you."

"You said you wanted to discuss terms," Lauri said suspiciously. "What sort of terms?"

"Not those sort, anyway." He gave a harsh laugh. "Credit me with some sense, Lauren," he snapped. "I'm hardly likely to want to seduce a teenager."

"But—"

"Oh, forget it, Lauren!" he said angrily. "I don't have any more time to discuss it. I don't know why the hell I should help you out anyway." He turned on his heel and walked off.

"Mr. Blair!" Lauri ran after him. "Mr. Blair, please—"

He either didn't hear her or didn't want to hear her, opening a door farther up the corridor and slamming the door in Lauri's face as she would have followed him inside. She had deserved that, she thought dully. Like he said, why should he help her? But he had been willing to, and she had thrown his offer back in his face.

She started guiltily as she heard the ascent of the lift, turning to confront her aunt. "Jane!" She sighed her relief that it wasn't someone else of importance who might also demand to know what she was doing up here.

"Lauri!" Jane looked shocked. "You shouldn't be up here."

She sighed, wishing she had never dared to brave the top floor. "I know."

"Then why are you?" Jane was obviously agitated by her presence here, looking about her almost guiltily. "If Mr. Blair or one of the managers should see you, you would have a hard time explaining what you're doing wandering around up here."

She already had! "You've got my purse," she said by way of explanation.

"I know that." Jane held it out to her. "I went downstairs to give it to you as soon as I realized."

"We must have missed each other." Lauri took the purse. "I'll have to go now; I'm late as it is."

"But, Lauri—"

She dived into the waiting lift, pressing the button. "See you later," she had time to call before the doors closed.

Phew! That was a narrow escape. Thank goodness Jane hadn't probed too deeply into why she had been standing aimlessly about in the corridor. If she had Lauri might have had to reveal that she had called the owner of the company arrogant, had accused him of being insulting and of tricking her into revealing she was a learner driver.

She might also have inadvertently revealed that Alexander Blair had invited her out to dinner, although invited was perhaps the wrong word to use. It had been an order, but a strange one, despite his assertion that he wanted to discuss terms for payment on the damage to his car. Terms! What could he mean by that? He had been furious at her assumption that he had any but the best intentions in mind, but she didn't think it could have been an entirely innocent suggestion. How on earth could she pay him back, unless he intended taking it from her wages, a little each week?

Perhaps that was what he had in mind, although surely he didn't need to invite her out to dinner to discuss that. Maybe he was at a loose end and wanted someone to amuse him for a few hours. And she had to admit, she certainly seemed to amuse him. Whatever his reason, she shouldn't have turned him down. He could make things pretty awkward for the whole of her family if he chose to.

It was for that reason, and that reason alone, that she decided to accept his dinner invitation. The trouble was telling him she had accepted!

She walked casually up to Carly's desk as she sat in her sectioned-off office, the partition walls consisting mainly of windows so that she could see what was going on in the outer office.

"Is there something wrong?" Carly looked up from the holiday rota she was working on.

"Er, no, not really. I—do you think I could use your telephone?" she said in a rush. "I know you've said in the past that we can, but I've never needed to bother before."

"Of course you can." Carly stood up to vacate the office to give her privacy for the call. "Give me a shout when you've finished."

"Thanks." Lauri gave her a grateful smile, relieved that her supervisor had shown no curiosity about who she would be telephoning.

She had to look up the number for Alexander Blair's office, aware that she would have to go through her aunt to speak to the man himself. Was it worth it, she asked herself. It had to be if it meant they all kept their jobs.

"Er, good morning," she said, deliberately deepening her voice and giving a husky sound to it that had sexual undertones as the telephone was suddenly answered by Jane."Could I speak to Alexander, please?" she asked in that same sexy voice.

For a moment there was silence, and Lauri wondered if her ruse had gone wrong. If Jane should guess it was her little niece on the line...! "Who shall I say is calling?" came Jane's businesslike reply.

Lauri heaved an inward sigh of relief. At least she hadn't been recognized yet. Now came the hard part. "Tell him it's...Lauren." After all he did call her that, and strangely, he was the only one ever to do so, giving an intimacy to their relationship that didn't exist.

"Lauren...?" Jane was obviously prompting for a surname.

"Just Lauren." She forced a provocative laugh. "He'll know who it is." She hoped! How awful if he demanded to know Lauren who?

"Very well." Jane sounded at her most haughty, which meant she wasn't pleased at being treated in this high-handed manner, even by someone she thought to be another of Alexander Blair's girl friends.

Did he have *girl* friends? She doubted it. He was much too sophisticated and sure of himself to tolerate naïveté in one of his women. No, he would go for women who knew exactly what they were doing, women who—.

"I'm putting you through now," Jane abruptly interrupted her thoughts.

Thank God he had remembered her. "Thank you so much," she replied in the sexy voice she had been using for the whole of the conversation.

"Glad to be of help," drawled the unmistakable voice of Alexander Blair. "Although this doesn't sound like the Lauren I know, and I haven't the faintest idea what I'm being thanked for."

"I wasn't thanking you!" she told him in her normal voice.

"Ah, that's better," he sounded mocking even over the telephone. "Why the change in voice?" he asked interestedly.

"I didn't want to be recognized. After all," she added hastily, "I do work here. I wouldn't want your secretary to make the connection between Lauri in the typing pool and the Lauren who just telephoned you."

"Is that likely?"

"I—well, it could be."

"I would doubt my secretary is any more familiar with the girls in the typing pool than I am," he drawled mockingly. "Would you?"

This girl she was! "Probably not," she evaded a direct answer. "But it wasn't worth the risk."

"Would it be too much to ask what this call is about? I thought it had been decided that your...friend was to take the blame for allowing you to drive his car."

"Yes, well I—I've been thinking, and—and—"

"And?" he prompted tersely.

"And if your invitation to dinner still stands, I would like to discuss...terms."

"It doesn't," he told her curtly. "Forget the dinner invitation."

"Oh." Her heart sank. She had been rude to him and he wasn't about to forgive such an insult from a nobody like her. "Please, Mr. Blair. I'm sorry for what I said. I—"

"The dinner invitation is out," he repeated. "But one for lunch today is open," he added inquiringly.

"Lunch today?" Her mouth gaped open and she quickly closed it again, realizing that although her conversation couldn't be heard by the girls outside the office, her reaction to it could clearly be seen.

"Well?" he rasped, pretty much as he had done after administering that punishing kiss yesterday.

"I—"

"Or do you usually have lunch with your boyfriend?" he interrupted before she could form an answer.

"Not always. Usually, but not always."

"Then today can be one of the exceptions." It sounded like an order. "I'll meet you in reception at twelve-thirty."

"No! No, Mr. Blair," she said more calmly. "I'd rather meet you somewhere away from here."

"I am not in the habit of sneaking out to meet anyone." His icy anger could quite easily be detected.

"Then perhaps you shouldn't take insignificant typists from your own typing pool to lunch." Her own anger equaled his. "That way you wouldn't have to sneak around."

"Lauren—" he began in a threatening tone.

"Okay, okay, I'm sorry," she sighed. "But you got angry first," she accused.

To her surprise she heard him chuckle, a rich deep sound

that made her feel like smiling, too. "Okay," he accepted. "I got angry first. But who made me angry, hmm?"

"I did," she freely admitted. "But try to understand, I don't want to be seen with you."

"Thanks!"

She sighed. "Will you stop misunderstanding everything I say?" she snapped.

"As long as you promise to stop reprimanding me," he returned smoothly.

"Reprimanding you? *Me*? Don't be ridiculous!"

"You see," he laughed. "You're doing it again."

At least he could laugh about it! "Sorry," she mumbled.

"You're forgiven," he said huskily soft. "And as you don't want to be seen with me—"

"I didn't mean that—"

"I know. Look, I don't have any more time to sit here chatting to you. Pleasant as it may be," he added mockingly. "I'll fall in with your wishes for the moment, and meet you at Marlo's at one o'clock. All right?"

Marlo's was a fashionable restaurant that had opened up a few months ago not far from here...and she knew her denims and pretty lawn blouse weren't suitable for such a place. "Couldn't we go somewhere less—less— I'm not dressed for it!" she told him crossly.

"No, you aren't, are you?" he mused. "Okay, I'll think of something else. Just meet me outside Marlo's at one. We'll go on somewhere else from there."

"But—"

"Do you ever stop arguing?" he sighed impatiently. "I'm not used to women who argue with me."

Then perhaps he should be, she thought bitchily. Alexander Blair was much too fond of his own way for her liking. "I argue with you because I'm not used to being ordered about," she said with great daring. "I like to be consulted, not told."

"Maybe that's why you can't hold on to your boy-friends," he remarked dryly. "The man likes to be in charge, Lauren, not the other way around."

"I can hold on to my boyfriends!" she told him angrily.

"Is that why the Canadian boy is deserting you at the end of the week, and Steve Prescott has been reduced to the level of a friend?"

"The reasons for Daryl leaving at the end of the week and Steve being a friend of mine are none of your business," Lauri told him with dignity. "I'm having to meet you to sort out the problem of your car, but that doesn't mean you have the right to ask personal questions."

To her consternation she heard him laugh. "My dear girl, I have no intention of asking you personal questions."

"But you—you did!" she accused.

"It was a question in the form of a statement, Lauren. Now, much as I'm enjoying this conversation," he said in a bored voice, his tone instantly giving lie to his words, "I have work to do. I'm sure you do, too. May I remind you that you're making this call on *my* time, and on the firm's telephone, no doubt?"

She flushed her guilt, glad he couldn't see her. "One o'clock, I think you said?"

"That's right." The line went dead as he rang off.

Lauri put the telephone down at her end, an angry sparkle to her glittering green eyes, a furious flush to her cheeks, her mouth set in a mutinous line. Bossy, overbear-ing— All the names she had previously called him seemed mild in comparison to what she wanted to call him now.

He was an arrogant swine! Just because he owned this firm, was her employer, didn't give him the right to treat her as if she had no more intelligence than a rather slow-witted child. If he thought he could talk to her in that manner and get away with it, then he was in for a shock. She—

Carly's wry chuckle broke in on her vehement thoughts. "I pity poor Daryl if he's the cause of all that anger," she teased, coming back into her office.

Lauri gave a start of surprise, so intense had been her dislike of Alexander Blair that she had forgotten where she was for the moment. She forced a smile to her lips, standing up to leave. "He doesn't need your pity," she told Carly tightly. And she didn't mean Daryl! "He's just too fond of having his own way."

"Aren't we all?" Carly smiled.

"Perhaps." But Alexander Blair had met his match in her, Lauri Prescott; she would make sure of that.

CHAPTER THREE

SHE FELT VERY CONSPICUOUS standing outside the restaurant at one o'clock, aware that she had received a few curious looks from people entering this fashionable eating house. It was ten-past one already; if Alexander Blair didn't turn up soon she was leaving.

As it was she had had another row with Daryl, this time about her not meeting him for lunch. She had told him she and Jane were going shopping, but he had wanted to know why she couldn't meet her aunt at five o'clock and do their shopping then. She had made the excuse that Jane might have to work late, hating having to lie to him, but at least he seemed to accept that explanation. Anyway, it could be the truth; Jane could be working late.

She looked down at her wristwatch. Another five minutes, that's all she would give him, and then she was off. If he thought she was going to stand about here waiting for him, then he was sadly—

"Are you going to get in?" drawled that infuriatingly familiar voice. "Or do you want me to get booked for illegal parking?"

Lauri looked over at the source of that voice; a low sleek black car, a Ferrari she thought, was parked next to the pavement. And Alexander Blair was seated behind the wheel. She had seen the car draw up, but as she was looking for a brown and gold Rolls-Royce, the arrival of this car had meant nothing to her, except to register what a fantastic car it was.

"I didn't realize it was you," she told him resentfully, moving to stand by the open window on the passenger side.

He gave her an impatient look. "Are you even going to argue about getting into the car?" he sighed.

"No, of course not!" She wrenched open the door and scrambled inside, at once sinking into the luxury—and intimacy—of the interior. Alexander Blair was much too close in the confines of such a car, making her aware of the tangy after-shave he wore and the much more basic male smell of him. "I was looking for the Rolls," she added stubbornly.

The car moved off smoothly under his expert handling, entering the flow of traffic leaving town. "The Rolls is badly dented, as you know."

"Yes." The word came out as a hiss. "But I wasn't to know you wouldn't still be driving it."

"It's in the garage being straightened out."

He hadn't even looked at her since she had got in the car, and she found herself glaring at him resentfully. "Rather quick, isn't it?" she snapped.

His mouth twisted tauntingly. "Some things can be arranged that way."

"If you have the money!"

His dark eyebrows rose. "Yes. I wouldn't have thought you the sort of girl to show prejudice because I happen to be rich."

She blushed at his rebuke, wondering just what sort of girl he *had* thought her to be, although she doubted he had actually given the matter a moment's thought. "I'm not," she agreed quietly. She grinned suddenly, her eyes sparkling mischievously. "Do I seem as if I've shown you any preferential treatment?"

A smile touched his mouth, a firm, controlled mouth

that didn't look as if it did much smiling. "None at all," he acknowledged.

"This is a lovely car, isn't it?" She forgot her hostility in that brief moment of shared humor. "Did the garage lend it to you while yours is being mended?" She remembered the old gray wreck Steve's garage had loaned him when Gerty had gone in for servicing last week. Gerty may be old, but even she was more reliable than that had been.

"Dare I admit that I own this car, too?" Alexander Blair mused, giving her a fleeting glance before turning his attention back to the road.

Her eyes widened. "You do? Oh, I much prefer this to a Rolls-Royce. A Rolls is so—so—"

"Respectable," he supplied mockingly. "It's meant to be. This car is for my own pleasure; it certainly wouldn't impress people with my reliability and good sense."

"Maybe not," Lauri agreed. "But it's much nicer." And made him appear more human!

He bowed mockingly. "I'm glad you approve," he drawled.

The car seemed to be literally eating up the miles and already they were well out of London. "Where are we going?" she asked curiously.

His mouth turned back. "Somewhere where my business suit and your denims won't look too out of place."

Lauri flushed, her good humor forgotten. "How was I to know I would be lunching with the exalted Alexander Blair?" she snapped. "If I had known I would have—"

"Dressed exactly the same," he interrupted smoothly. "At my request."

Her eyes widened. "You—your request?"

"Mmm. You look lovely in denims, Lauren, much better than any other female I know."

"Oh." She blushed profusely.

He gave a sudden burst of laughter. "Don't tell me I've actually rendered you speechless. I don't believe it!"

But he had. His sudden compliment had come as a complete surprise to her. There was no doubt that it had been a compliment; the warmth in those startling blue eyes as he looked at her making it impossible for it to be anything else. Alexander Blair had paid *her* a compliment!

"I can see I have," he mused. "Amazing! I can see I'll have to take advantage of this temporary loss of voice on your part—and I feel sure it can only be temporary—by telling you that it was my suit I felt would be out of place. A necessary evil during business hours, I'm afraid."

But it was such a nice suit; its fit and cut superb, the cream color emphasizing the dark tan he had acquired on his recent trip to America. Lauri found herself staring at him, unashamedly admiring his good looks. It seemed she saw him for the first time, always too angry before to realize just how devastatingly attractive his features were, or to realize how potent was the sexual aura he seemed to emit from every pore of his body. But now she was aware of it, too much so, in fact. She looked away, confused by her own sudden weakness toward a man she had thought she disliked.

"Lauren?" His husky query made her tremble with her new awareness of him. "Lauren?" he prompted again at her continued silence.

She frowned. "Why do you call me that? I told you that everyone calls me Lauri."

"I'm not everyone," he told her softly. "I don't want to be grouped with the herd."

She almost laughed at the ridiculousness of that statement. He could never be anything but the forceful individual he was. "But no one else bothers to call me Lauren," she persisted.

"Exactly." He was out of the car and helping her out of her side before she had hardly had time to realize they had stopped. "Come on, let's eat."

Lauri saw they had stopped outside an attractive little pub, several tables and chairs standing in the picturesque garden at the back. It was to one of these tables that Alexander Blair led her.

"What would you like to drink?" he asked once she was seated. "I'll bring the menu back with me."

"How do you know they serve food?" She hadn't seen any sign up to say they did.

He smiled. "I've been here before."

"Oh."

"With my sister," he supplied tauntingly.

"Your *sister*?"

"Yes." He was openly laughing at her now. "She lives a couple of miles from here. Your drink?" he prompted.

"Lemonade, please," she requested reluctantly.

"Lemonade?" His disgust was obvious.

"I—I can't drink at lunchtime; it gives me a headache, and I can't work properly in the afternoon when that happens."

"In that case I'll get the lemonade," he teased. "I can't have one of my employees slacking."

"I—I'll just have a sandwich to eat, thank you. Ham or something like that," she said shyly, aware that her feelings toward this man had changed drastically since this morning. Just to look at him made her tingle all over.

"Don't tell me you have to watch your figure," he scorned. "Aren't there enough of us males already doing that?"

Lauri frowned. "I don't know what you mean. There's only Daryl—"

"And Steve. And me," he added huskily.

The look in her eyes was uncertain. "You?" she repeated breathlessly, feeling curiously as if she had swum too far and was now out of her depth.

"I'd have to have looked at you pretty closely to know how good you look in denims," he pointed out. "You're all long legs and slender hips. And then there's your—"

"Please!" Her face was scarlet with embarrassment. "I— Just lemonade and a sandwich," she repeated, turning away to look fixedly at the riot of flowers that edged the lawn the tables and chairs stood on.

He didn't leave immediately, and Lauri was aware of his gaze on her for several long minutes more, although she refused to turn and meet that look. Finally he moved away and Lauri turned to watch him as he entered the saloon bar. He had to duck his head to get in the low doors, and then she could hear the low murmur of voices as he gave their order.

What was he trying to do to her? Why the compliments, the almost flirtatious manner? She didn't trust him in this mood; she wanted to get back to work and away from the power he was exerting over her. No man had ever reduced her to such a nervous state before, and she didn't like it.

"Here." Alexander Blair put a glass down on the table in front of her. "It's shandy." He gave a rueful smile. "I just couldn't bring myself to ask for a glass of lemonade." He sat down beside her, a glass of whiskey in his hand.

An unwilling smile lightened her features. "I should think it's unheard of for you."

"I couldn't even get the word to pass my lips," he smiled back at her.

And they were such firm sensual lips, too, curved in a half smile now as he watched her with narrowed blue eyes. "The shandy will be fine, thank you."

"I ordered you a steak and salad," He sipped his whiskey. "I hope that meets your approval."

"Of course. But a sandwich would have done." She couldn't help noticing the way the sun made his hair appear blacker than ever, a bluish sheen to the overlong styled hair; she wrenched her gaze away as he became conscious of her scrutiny.

"I don't take a girl out to lunch and give her a sandwich," he said disgustedly. "We'll go inside when our meal is ready."

"You've hardly brought me out to lunch through choice," Lauri derided. "We're here to discuss the damage I did to your car."

"Has your ... friend—" again that hesitation "—has Prescott had his car looked at yet?"

"He took it round to a friend of his last night. He did the repairs on the brakes."

"The brakes?" Alexander Blair frowned.

"Mmm," she nodded, sipping her drink. "You see, Steve had the car serviced last week. He told them the brakes weren't responding properly, but they couldn't find anything wrong with them. Steve's mate Geoff found the problem and put it right."

Alexander Blair was still frowning. "Is that why you—"

"Hit you?" she finished. "Yes. Nothing happened when I tried to stop."

"Is that the truth?"

Color flooded her cheeks: "I have no reason to lie," she said stiltedly.

"Maybe you think I'll let you off the hook if you can convince me it was through a fault in the car that the accident happened."

Her glass landed on the table with a crash, surprisingly still intact. "You arrogant—"

"Now, now, Lauren," he laughed, putting up his hands defensively. "Don't get violent."

"I have no intention of getting violent," she told him through tight lips.

"I never know what you're going to do when you get that angry sparkle in those huge green eyes of yours. They're very expressive, Lauren. At the moment they're hating me, am I right?"

"Yes," she admitted tautly. "I resent your implication that I would lie to get myself out of taking responsibility for your car. I'm perfectly willing to pay for the damage if you'll settle this privately."

"Prescott shouldn't have let you drive without L-plates," he told her haughtily. "He was in charge of you *and* the vehicle, so it's his responsibility. Anyway, why should you care? After all, he's only a friend."

"If that's all the concern you show for your own friends, then I'm surprised you still have any," she snapped.

"Was he your lover before he became a friend?"

Lauri gasped. "Certainly not!" she retorted indignantly.

"Why wasn't he?"

"Mr. Blair, you have no right—"

"Alex," he put in softly.

She frowned. "Alex?"

"Call me Alex," he invited.

"I will not!" she refused angrily. "Steve was never my lover," she insisted.

"I know," Alexander Blair told her calmly.

Her eyes widened. "You know? Then why did you—How do you know?" she asked suspiciously.

The barmaid came out at that moment to tell them their meal was ready inside, and so Lauri didn't immediately get an answer to her question. She had to wait until they had been seated at a table inside and their appetizing meal placed before them before she could repeat the question.

"Not while I'm eating, Lauren," Alex refused to answer her.

"We can talk in between eating."

He looked at his wristwatch. "You have fifteen minutes before your lunch break is up. I'm willing to allow you a few minutes extra to eat that meal, but certainly not so that you can talk."

"Oh, but—"

"Eat, Lauren," he ordered firmly.

With a resentful glare in his direction she did as he told her, finding the steak and salad to her liking—despite her dining companion. He must be used to much more sophisticated surroundings, and yet he appeared to be completely at his ease, complimenting the barmaid on the food before their departure, causing a blush to come to the young girl's cheeks.

"Mr. Blair," Lauri began once they were on their way again. "Mr. Blair, I—"

"Alex. We agreed it should be Alex," he murmured huskily.

"We agreed to no such thing!"

He gave an impatient sigh. "I've never known anyone like you for arguing. It must be that red hair."

"It isn't red!" she flared up once again.

He gave her a considering look. "No, it isn't," he slowly agreed. "It's very beautiful. Red gold." He frowned suddenly. "You remind me of someone, you know, Lauren."

"I—I do?" If he could see any resemblance between herself and either her aunt or uncle, then he was the first one ever to do so.

"Mmm," he nodded. "But I can't think who for the moment. No doubt it will come to me, probably when I see the other person again."

"It's a sign of advancing years when the memory starts to go." She was deliberately provocative in an effort to divert his attention from who she resembled.

It seemed she had hit home, his mouth tightening angrily. "I didn't say I couldn't remember, only that I can't yet see what the resemblance is, the certain something that occasionally sparks off a memory of someone else doing exactly the same thing."

She licked her lips. "I see. Well, you still haven't answered my question," she reminded.

"About Prescott being your lover?" He smiled. "But how could he be when he's your uncle?"

Lauri gulped, her face paling. "You—you know?"

He laughed. "Of course."

"How long have you known?" she demanded indignantly.

Alex shrugged. "Since yesterday."

"You've known all the time and you—"

"I didn't say all the time," he disputed calmly. "Only since the afternoon when I looked up your file. You forget, until that time I didn't even know what your name was, only that it wasn't Lauri. You see, there's a Laura in your department, too. I had no way of knowing which you were until you told me you were Lauren."

"You looked up my file?" She was incredulous.

He nodded. "I went down to personnel and had a look."

"Then you also know—"

"That my invaluable secretary, the efficient Miss Prescott, is your aunt," he finished for her. "Yes, I know that,
too. Which brings me to the point of why you put on that
false voice over the telephone this morning. Not that I'm
complaining," he grinned. "It sounded very sexy, and in
the right circumstances...well, who knows? But by that
little act and by the fact that your aunt has been her usual
coolly pleasant self, I've come to the conclusion that she
knows nothing of your little escapade in her brother's car
yesterday morning."

Once again he had rendered Lauri speechless. Was there
nothing this man didn't know or couldn't find out?

"Am I right?" he persisted.

"You know you are," she said miserably.

"I thought so. She wouldn't be pleased?"

"What do you think?"

Alex laughed. "She wouldn't be pleased at all."

"She would be furious."

"Mmm. So I have you in my power, do I?"

Lauri gave him a sharp look. "I wouldn't go that far."

"Oh, I would. My Miss Prescott, and I don't mean
you—"

"That's good, because I'm not yours. And I don't think
Jane would like being called that, either. Spoken to anyone
else but me that remark might have been misconstrued.
You really should be more careful about what you say, Mr.
Blair."

She heard him draw an angry breath. "You are without
doubt the most outspoken young lady I've ever met. I don't
know why I'm wasting my time on you."

"Neither do I," she retorted, seeing they were nearing
the Blair office block. "Could you drop me off here,
please," she pleaded. "I—I'll walk the rest of the way."

"So that you aren't seen with me?" he taunted.

"Yes!" She met his speculative look defiantly.

"What's it worth?" he queried softly.

"What's it— What do you mean?"

He quirked an eyebrow. "What do you think I mean?" He had slowed the car right down. "If you arrive back with me then *my* Miss Prescott will no doubt get to hear about it—and I bet you're willing to do quite a lot to stop that happening. Tell me, does she frighten you as much as she frightens me?"

"*Jane* frightens you?"

"Terrifies me."

"Liar!" She laughed.

"Maybe. But she's certainly a formidable lady. She won't stand any nonsense."

"Are you telling me that you've made a *pass* at my Aunt Jane?" Lauri exclaimed.

"Heaven forbid!" he drawled in mock horror. "She would soon put me firmly in my place. I daren't make a wrong move with that lady, and I would make a guess that you daren't, either. I think crashing into my car constitutes a wrong move, don't you?"

"Yes," she admitted reluctantly.

"So, what's it worth?" he repeated.

"I don't know what you mean," she evaded.

"Oh, I think you do, Lauren," he taunted.

"No." She desperately shook her head. "No, I don't. I certainly don't consider the accident and keeping it from Jane reason enough to—to— I'd rather tell her everything than sink to that level!"

"Why, what do you mean, Miss Prescott?" He feigned shock. "I was merely suggesting you agree to have dinner with me; certainly nothing else."

"Have dinner with you?" she repeated dazedly.

"Yes." He stopped the car at the side of the road, turning to look at her. "Will you come?"

"But I— We've only just had lunch."

"Well, I wasn't suggesting we have dinner now," he smiled. "Later tonight will do."

"I have a date," she told him stiffly.

"With your Canadian?"

"With Daryl, yes."

"And as he departs at the end of the week I don't suppose I should deprive him of your company. After all, I'll have you to myself when he's gone."

"Mr. Blair...."

"Yes, Lauren?" He smoothed a lock of hair back from her face. "I like your freckles," he murmured, his eyes intent on her face.

Lauri blushed under his scrutiny. "You—you do?"

"Mmm, they're adorable. They make me want to kiss the tip of that little snub nose of yours."

She flinched away. "Mr. Blair! Stop playing games with me."

He watched her with laughter in his eyes. "Is that what I'm doing?"

"You know it is. But I won't be used for your amusement. I'm not going to let you laugh at me, you—you—"

Alex shook his head. "I'm not laughing at you, Lauren. In fact, I don't find any of this funny. How long have you worked for me?"

"Why?" she asked curiously.

He sighed. "How long?"

"Three weeks," she supplied.

He nodded. "That accounts for my not having seen you before. I didn't think I could have overlooked you."

She gave a nervous laugh, still conscious of his hand in her hair. "I'm quite overlookable."

Alex shook his head. "Not by me you aren't. You've been forcing yourself into my thoughts ever since we met yesterday. And that's why I don't find this situation funny. You're eighteen, just, and I'm a man of thirty-four, and yet I can't get you off my mind." He gave a derisive smile. "It must be that startling combination of red gold hair and defiant green eyes. Whatever it is, it's pretty explosive to my equilibrium. So I intend seeing you as often as possible in an effort to get you out of my system."

"And if I don't want to see *you*?" She was furious at his assumption that she would be willing to see any more of him than she had to. Not that she believed his wild assertion that he wanted to see her to get over his attraction to her; there had to be another reason. Maybe there was another woman in his life he wanted to get rid of and he intended using Lauri to do it. What woman wouldn't be piqued to find he preferred a nonentity like Lauri Prescott to their undoubtable beauty and sophistication. Yes, that had to be it, and she wasn't going to help him out. It may help him to be seen with her, but it could only bring trouble to her. She found him attractive enough already without making the mistake of falling for him!

Alex shrugged. "I could always tell your aunt of your... accident, of the fact that you weren't showing L-plates. I don't think she would appreciate that last part."

Remembering how Jane was always telling her to curb her impetuosity, Lauri didn't think she would, either. "Don't you have any other way of getting rid of her?" Lauri scorned.

He looked puzzled. "Your aunt? But I don't want—"

Lauri sighed. "Not Jane. The woman you don't want in your life, the woman you're using me to put off."

He laughed. "You're that woman, Lauren, no one else."

"I don't believe you. It's ridiculous."

"I couldn't agree more," he grimaced.

"Well, there's no need to be insulting about it," Lauri snapped. "You really do, er, like me?"

He smiled at her choice of word. "I find you very... desirable."

"Me?" she squeaked.

Alex nodded. "You. But in my experience familiarity always leads to contempt."

"So that's why you want to go out with me. Thanks very much!"

"Would you rather the attraction developed?" he taunted. "I'm warning you, I usually expect a physical relationship from my women. I'm way past the hand-holding, chaste-kisses age. So I'm hoping to kill this attraction toward you stone dead before it gets to the stage where I take you to my bed."

"I'd never allow it to get that far," Lauri told him coldly. "I suppose I can take solace from the fact that it shouldn't take you long to get bored with me. I'm a little immature for your tastes."

"Your immaturity doesn't stop you being downright rude on occasions," he snapped.

"It's because I am immature that I dare to be rude. If I was older I'd have more sense than to try and cross you."

"I'm glad you realize it wouldn't pay to push me too far," he said grimly. "We'll have dinner together on Saturday," he told her arrogantly.

"And your car; what's going to happen about that?"

"We'll forget about it. After all, it wouldn't be very chivalrous of me to try and extract money from the girl I'm taking out."

"But—but we can't just forget it," she protested. "It must be costing a fortune."

He quoted a figure that made her gasp. "Do you have that sort of money?"

"It's really costing that much?" she croaked.

He nodded. "Really."

"Goodness!"

"Quite," he drawled. "Don't tell me you're speechless again?"

"I don't talk that much that a little silence from me should be treated with derision," Lauri snapped. "I don't believe a word you say about being attracted to me; you're much too mocking toward me for it to be true."

Alex gave a husky laugh. "What do you expect me to do? Grant you your every wish like some besotted idiot?"

"Certainly not!" she said disgustedly.

"Thank God for that." His hand moved to ruffle her hair. "Be ready at eight o'clock Saturday night."

"But—"

"No more objections, Lauren," he said impatiently. "Are you aware of the fact that your lunch hour was just up?"

"It can't be!" A hurried look at her watch confirmed that it was. "Oh, damn, Carly won't be very pleased."

He quirked an eyebrow. "Carly?"

"My supervisor," she informed him vaguely.

He nodded. "Carly Hammond. I'll okay it with her."

That he actually knew Carly's full name came as something of a surprise to her. After all, he was a man with hundreds, if not thousands, of employees. But she certainly couldn't let him "okay" anything, even though she felt sure he would do it very tactfully.

Alexander Blair was a man who let very little stand in his

way when he wanted something, and for the moment he seemed to want her. If she dared to admit it to herself, she was secretly excited about the prospect of being escorted by such a man. Never in her wildest dreams had she ever thought such a man would show interest in her, and now that he had, for whatever reason, she knew she wanted to go out with him. She could still vividly remember that hard, savage kiss he had given her in the lift—and she was wondering if it would ever be repeated! Besides, if she must qualify her actions any further, he was being very generous about the damage to his car. Not that she really needed any further excuse to agree to see him!

"Lauren?" he tersely interrupted her daydreaming.

"Sorry." She gave him a guilty look, hoping he wasn't able to guess what her thoughts had been. Those piercing blue eyes seemed to miss nothing. "I'll make my own excuses to Carly, thank you."

"So prim!" He smiled mockingly. "I think you'll find it will pass off a lot easier coming from me."

"And I'm equally sure it won't," she said with saccharin sweetness. "It's perfectly all right; Carly won't read me the riot act. She doesn't happen to rule with an iron will." Her tone implied that she left that sort of thing to people like him.

His eyes narrowed. "With a little spitfire like you I think she ought to."

Lauri gave him a cold look. "I happen to respect Carly's authority," she retorted.

"And it's pretty damned obvious you don't respect mine!" His eyes were glittering with a dangerous anger that made Lauri move nearer to the door. "Well, respect *this*!" His hand snaked out to curl about her nape, pulling her resistingly forward, grabbing a handful of her fiery hair to pull her head back. He moved with slow deliberation, enjoying the torment in her eyes before his mouth claimed hers.

Lauri felt as if she were drowning, that her body was no longer her own but was part of Alexander Blair's as he ravaged her lips with a hunger that devoured her very soul. No one had ever kissed her like this. His mouth demanded her surrender to his domination, to the male sensuality of him.

And she was surrendering, offering no resistance as he pushed her back against the seat, his body half covering hers as he made her aware of the desire he couldn't hold in check, the clamoring of his senses for fulfillment.

But it was Alex who finally became aware of the fact that the car was parked on the side of a particularly busy road, and that they were providing a free show for the passersby. He moved back into his own seat, pushing his tousled hair back with hands that weren't quite steady.

"You see," he muttered grimly, his breathing ragged. "I told you you're explosive to my equilibrium—for equilibrium read sexual urges."

"Yes." She was totally breathless, dazed by his fierce lovemaking.

Alex eyed her impatiently. "You have a way of saying that word that makes me wish we were in more suitable surroundings."

"Like a bedroom."

"Exactly!" he sighed. "This is hardly the way I should be behaving in the middle of the street!" He sounded disgusted with himself.

"And with a little typist, too," she taunted to cover her confusion. She hadn't given a damn where they were a few minutes ago—she had just wanted him to go on kissing her.

He didn't rise to her taunt. Some of the angry tension left

his body as he smiled. "I thought all good bosses had affairs with their secretaries. It's traditional, you know."

"I'm not your secretary, and we are not having an affair!" She glared at him, her usual fiery nature returning to save her from making a fool of herself. She had been totally shaken by that kiss.

"True," he acknowledged. "But have you learned to respect *my* authority yet?" He reminded her of the remark that had challenged him to that devastating reaction.

She thought of defying him yet again, but didn't dare incite another of those shattering kisses. "Yes," she said quietly.

"And you'll admit that there is an attraction between us and go out with me willingly?"

"Yes," she agreed huskily. There was no point in denying the attraction. He would only have to kiss her again to find that out, and being attracted to him she *wanted* to go out with him.

Alex shook his head in a dazed fashion. "You never say what I expect you to say," he mused. "Maybe that's why I find you so intriguing. You won't bore me, Lauren," he denied her earlier claim. "You're much too unpredictable for that."

"I really will have to go now." She avoided getting into a discussion about how he felt about her, anxious to get away from the male magnetism of him.

He nodded. "Sure you don't want me to explain to Miss Hammond?"

"You'll only make matters worse."

"About Saturday." He stopped her hasty flight. "Am I allowed to pick you up at your home."

"No!"

"Then where?" he mocked.

"I—I'll meet you at the end of my road. You must understand," she said desperately at his look of anger. "It could make things very awkward if people knew we were going out together, especially for Jane. Think how she would feel if she knew you were dating her niece. Besides, it could be very embarrassing for you, too."

"I don't give a damn about me. My employees are paid to work, not to speculate about my private life."

"But they do. Please don't—"

"God, this is farcical!" he exploded. "Look, I'll tell your aunt if it will make it easier for you."

"Don't you dare!" she told him fiercely. "If you do that I—I'll refuse to go anywhere with you," she threatened heatedly.

"I thought you said you would go out with me willingly," he reminded. "That you respected my ... authority."

"Not to that extent," Lauri snapped adamantly.

"All right," he sighed his defeat. "Saturday." He placed a brief kiss on her stubborn mouth. "And don't keep me waiting, or I'm likely to come looking for you."

Lauri hurried back to the office, claiming she had been shopping and had forgotten the time. As she had never been late before, Carly accepted her explanation without question—much to Lauri's relief. What on earth would Carly have said if she had known the real reason for her lateness!

CHAPTER FOUR

"COME ON, STEVE," Lauri said complainingly. "It's your turn to wash up. You may be the only male in the household, but that doesn't mean you get out of all the work around here."

He got up with a grimace, taking the tea towel out of her hand. "I'm sure it's Jane's turn."

"It may be," she agreed. "But she's getting ready for her date with Robin."

"Well, I'm going out, too," he moaned.

"Only to Geoff's," she scorned.

Steve frowned. "You don't think Jane is really serious about Robin, do you?"

Lauri shrugged. "I don't know. You know she never discusses anything like that with us."

"I hope she isn't," he grimaced. "I can't stand the man. His sense of humor is nonexistent."

"It only seems that way because yours is overdeveloped," said a sufferer of his pranks for years. "He can't help it if he doesn't appreciate our warped sense of humor. The poor man feels overwhelmed by us every time he comes here, I'm sure he does. Anyway, if he makes Jane happy, that's all we should worry about." She put the crockery away as he dried it.

"But does he make her happy? I haven't seen much evidence of it."

"She wouldn't see him if she didn't like him." Lauri evaded giving him a direct answer, not at all sure herself of Jane's feelings for Robin. She had been seeing him for some time now, and Robin seemed serious about her, but Jane was as noncommittal as ever.

"I suppose not. Although I really hope he isn't Mr. Right. She could do a lot better for herself than him. Talking of someone better, Mr. Blair got in touch with me this afternoon."

Her face colored fiery red and then paled, and she made a pretense of tidying a cupboard so that Steve shouldn't see her reaction to just the mention of their employer's name. "Did he?" she asked casually.

"Mmm. Now there's someone I wouldn't mind Jane getting serious about. Do you think she likes him?" he queried interestedly.

Lauri shrugged. How would Steve feel if he knew that it wasn't Jane who was being dated by Alexander Blair, but her niece? "She's never mentioned him as anything other than her boss."

"But that doesn't mean she isn't interested in him. Now he's what I call a man worthy of my big sister. He's a really great bloke."

"Why?" she asked dryly.

He grinned. "Because he's decided to forget about the damage to his car."

Alex hadn't wasted much time in letting Steve know that! Now she was really committed to seeing him. Maybe that was why he had done it; perhaps he had thought she might change her mind. "So your partiality is purely mercenary," she taunted.

"Not completely, although that does come into it. The damage to his car must be costing a fortune."

It was. She couldn't tell Steve just how much—if she did, she would have to reveal how she came to know—but the amount still staggered her. That Alex was willing to write that amount off just proved how very rich he was. If she had needed any confirmation!

Jane came down from her bedroom and Lauri shot her uncle a warning glance. Luckily he saw that look before making any revealing remarks.

"Will you zip me up, please?" Jane came to stand in front of Lauri. "Thanks," she said as Lauri obliged.

"Are you feeling better today?" she asked her aunt.

"Much," Jane nodded. "Mr. Blair seems to have got over his mood, although first thing this morning I thought it was going to be another of those days." She smiled. "His mood changed after his girl friend called him."

Steve's eyes widened. "You actually spoke to Connie Mears?" he sounded astounded.

Jane shook her head. "It would appear she has been replaced." She sat down to wait for Robin. "This girl has an incredibly sexy voice."

"Who is she, another actress?" Steve wanted to know.

His sister shrugged. "I have no idea. She just introduced herself as Lauren."

Steve gave Lauri a sharp look, but luckily she managed to meet that searching look with a completely bland expression.

"She must have arranged to meet him for lunch," Jane continued. "Because he came back from lunch in a really good mood."

"What did I tell you about lunchtime sessions?" Steve joked, having obviously dismissed the idea of this Lauren being his little niece, Lauri.

"Steve!" Jane frowned at him. "I won't have you talking

about Mr. Blair like that. In future I shall revert to not telling you anything about him.'' She stood up as the doorbell rang. "That will be Robin. I'll see you both later.''

"No wonder he let me off paying for his car," Steve said once he and Lauri were alone again. "She must be really something, his girl friend.''

"Yes.'' She pretended interest in the newspaper.

"For a minute I thought it was you when Jane mentioned someone called Lauren.''

She forced a light laugh, making herself look at him. "Now is that likely? Besides, I would hardly describe my voice as sexy, would you?''

"Maybe not to me, but then I have no idea how you would talk to a man you're attracted to.''

"Who says I'm attracted to Alex Blair?'' she asked sharply.

"Alex?" he questioned sharply.

Lauri blushed. "All right, *Alexander* Blair.''

"But you called him Alex," Steve persisted with a frown.

"Why not?" She gave a casual shrug. "I'm sure his name gets shortened.''

"Maybe. But I've never heard anyone do it—until now. *Were* you the Lauren who telephoned him?'' he asked suspiciously.

"Don't be ridiculous, Steve. You know that no one ever calls me Lauren. I'm always Lauri to my friends.''

"Yes, but—''

She jumped up as the doorbell rang for the second time that evening. "That will be Daryl for me. And I thought you were going to Geoff's,'' she prompted as she went to the door.

"Is that a polite way of saying you want to be alone with him?''

She quirked an eyebrow. "What do you think?" Thank goodness he seemed to have forgotten Alex—Alexander Blair for the moment. She would have to make sure she didn't make that sort of slip again.

"I hope you intend behaving yourself," Steve warned. "I wouldn't want you to do anything stupid just because he's leaving at the end of the week."

"Who is?" Her thoughts had been miles away—with Alex Blair.

"Daryl is," he said impatiently. "Your boyfriend, the person leaning heavily on the doorbell at this very moment."

"Oh—oh, yes. And if by anything stupid you mean what I think you mean, you can forget it. I'm not interested in Daryl that way." Only one man had the power to excite her to the point of forgetting everything else but him, to make her forget all the morals Jane had taken pains to instill in her.

"How about Alex?" Steve taunted.

She blushed uncomfortably. Many more questions like this and she would give herself away completely. Damn Alex Blair and his potent kisses! *"Alexander,"* she corrected cheekily, opening the door to admit Daryl.

She forced herself to accept Daryl's greeting kiss, aware that her response was a trifle strained. After Alex Blair's kisses she couldn't bring herself to give Daryl any more than the mildest of caresses.

"Are you feeling okay?" he asked her once Steve had taken his leave and they were alone.

She avoided looking at him. "I'm fine. Maybe a little tired."

"Oh, only you seem preoccupied."

"Sorry." She gave him a bright smile. "Steve and I have

just been wondering if Jane is serious about her boyfriend. I suppose I'm still thinking about it," she lied.

"I see. Do you think she is?"

Lauri laughed. "I have no idea. Steve was more worried about it than I was. I just want Jane to be happy."

Daryl frowned. "Talking of Jane, I thought you said you were going shopping with her at lunchtime?"

Another lie, but she had had to make some excuse for not joining him. "Yes," she answered warily.

"Then why didn't you? I saw her eating her lunch in the canteen. She was with a couple of the other secretaries, so I didn't speak to her."

"Actually she...she had to work at the last minute," Lauri said hastily. "No doubt she was just snatching a quick meal before going back up to her office."

"She didn't look in any hurry to me."

"What's that supposed to mean?" she queried sharply, attack the best form of defense in this case. "What are you implying?"

"Why, nothing." He looked surprised by her aggressive tone. "I just wondered why you didn't let me know, and then we could have gone to lunch together as usual."

"I went shopping anyway. I—I had some things to get."

"I could still have come with you," he complained.

"Well, I didn't think of it," she snapped impatiently. "Is it that important?" She knew she was being bitchy, but she couldn't seem to help it.

"It doesn't appear to be to you," he said almost sulkily. "But as I'm only going to be around another three days I thought, mistakenly, that you might want to spend as much time with me as possible. It seems I was wrong." He stood up. "Would you like me to leave?"

"Don't be silly, Daryl." She felt guilty about her treat-

ment of him. Alexander Blair may have her totally confused with his male magnetism, but that was no reason to
take it out on Daryl. "Sit down and we'll listen to some
records."

"Well...if you're sure?"

"I'm sure." It was about the only thing she was sure of!

SHE WAS JUST AS BAD the next day; her work output nowhere
up to standard. How could she have agreed to go out with
Alexander Blair on Saturday? It was an act of sheer madness on her part. He had openly admitted he was only seeing her so that he would tire of her. How flattering that was!

Why was it that men like him, men who threw their inde-
pendence from women out as a challenge to any red-
blooded female, had the power to captivate? But he wasn't
just a challenge to her, although his remark about familiarity leading to contempt still rankled; he really did attract her
most strongly. She wasn't even sure she liked him as a person—he was much too arrogant and dictatorial for her independent nature, but he only had to kiss her to get her to
agree to anything he suggested. As long as he didn't suggest
they sleep together she should be all right!

"Telephone call for you, Lauri," Carly called over to her.

She looked up with a frown. She never received calls here.
"Male or female?" she asked before going into the office.

Carly grinned. "Oh, definitely male."

"Daryl?"

Her supervisor shrugged. "Could be. He didn't say."

"Okay. Thanks." She picked up the receiver. "Yes?"

"Lauren?"

"Al, er, hello," she quavered, conscious of Carly standing a few feet away, able to hear her side of the conversation at least.

"Is there someone in the room with you?" Alexander Blair demanded to know at her restraint. "Carly Hammond, perhaps?"

Well, it was her office for goodness' sake! "Yes."

"Get rid of her," he growled.

She gave an angry gasp. "That isn't possible."

"Of course it is," he snapped impatiently. "Just tell her to get out."

"I can't do that," she refused firmly. "But thank you for calling. I—I'll get back to you later in the week." When she would give him a piece of her mind!

"Don't put this phone down, Lauren," he warned. "If you do I'll come down to the typing pool. Do you want that?"

"No!" she told him furiously. "You know I don't."

"Then get rid of her. How the hell can I have a conversation with you with her listening to your end of it?"

"Perhaps it would have been better if you hadn't called here. I'm sure you have my home number."

"You know damn well I have, but you wouldn't have liked my calling you there, either. Carly Hammond may not have recognized my voice, but I can assure you your Aunt Jane would have no trouble doing so. Perhaps it's as well Carly is there; you can ask her for the afternoon off."

"Don't be stu— That's impossible." She held on to her temper with effort.

"I'll make it possible. Put her on to me."

"No," she refused angrily. "I can't get away. It's too late in the day to make the arrangements."

"Put her on, Lauren," he ordered firmly.

"No, I won't." She gave Carly a resigned shrug, putting her hand over the mouthpiece. "Sorry about this," she murmured. "Some people are so persistent."

"Do you need some time off?" Carly asked sympathetically.

"Well, I—" She didn't want to give in to this autocratic man, and yet she didn't want him coming down here, either.

"Lauren?" Alex queried tersely. "What's going on? Have you asked her?"

"No, and I don't intend to." She put the receiver down. How dare he take that attitude with her. Her youthfully confident nature rebelled against such arrogance.

"Something wrong?" Carly was watching her curiously.

"Some people think I have nothing better to do..." she mumbled, scowling. "I— Would you mind if I went to lunch now?" She knew she didn't have much time to get out of here before Alex arrived. She had no doubt he would carry out his threat to come down to the typing pool.

"Of course not," Carly readily agreed. "Are you sure you don't need some time off?"

Not if it meant she looked as if she were giving Alex what he wanted. "I just need my lunch," she smiled.

"Persistent boyfriend?"

She shook her head. "A forgotten dental appointment. I conveniently forgot the last one, too."

"You can still go. We aren't too busy this afternoon."

"No, thanks. I have an aversion to dentists. Just the thought of it has made me feel ill. I'll see you later." She collected her jacket and handbag and made a hurried exit. If Alex came down here she intended being conspicuous in her absence.

"And just where do you think you're going?" A hand shot out and stopped her progress...and she didn't need two guesses who her assailant was.

She slowly turned to face Alexander Blair. "I'm going to

lunch,'' she told him defiantly. Heavens, he looked hand
some today! The iron-gray suit fitted him perfectly, th
white silk shirt taut across his muscular chest.

His eyes narrowed to blue slits. "To avoid me?"

She met that look without flinching. "What do yo
think?"

The anger seemed to ebb out of him. "I think," he sai
huskily soft, "that you look beautiful when you're angry
There's a slight flush to your creamy cheeks, and you'r
eyes are sparkling like emeralds.''

That flush changed to a brilliant blush. "Don't chang
the subject!" Already she could feel herself weakening to
ward him. Damn the man!

"*You* are the subject." The warmth in his gaze was ur
mistakably desire.

Lauri looked about them self-consciously. Luckily the
were the only two people in the corridor, but they couldn
be that lucky for long, and if someone should see ther
together.... "I'm going to lunch." She turned on her hee
and walked off.

Alex fell into step beside her. "What a coincidence," h
grinned. "So am I."

Lauri came to a halt, glaring at him furiously. "Not wit
me, you aren't."

He quirked an eyebrow. "Willingly, I thought you said.

She flushed. "That was for Saturday."

He shrugged. "So, I wanted to see you before then."

"You've seen me, now leave me alone."

His hand came out to grasp her arm. "You don't mea
that."

She trembled. "But I do!" she insisted forcefully, know
ing just how weak she sounded.

"Like me to prove otherwise?" Alex taunted.

She remembered only too well the way he had proved her attraction to him the last time. "Not here, Alex," she pleaded.

He smiled. "For calling me Alex so naturally I'll let you off—for the moment." There was a promise in this last comment. "But you are having lunch with me," he added firmly.

"No—"

"Yes!" His grip tightened. "I'll meet you outside in the car park in five minutes. And remember, I couldn't give a damn about people knowing about us, so if you aren't there in that five minutes I'll come looking for you."

"I'm having lunch with Daryl," she said desperately.

"Not anymore you aren't. I need you more than he does."

"You...you need me?"

He nodded grimly. "You're becoming a necessary part of my day. Saturday was too damned far away. Daryl will just have to learn to do without you."

"Not because you say so!" Her rebellious nature surfaced again. "I don't—" She broke off as a man from the accounts department came toward them. "No, I'm sorry, Mr. Blair, I have no idea where my aunt could be." The glitter in her eyes dared him to refute her effort to provide an excuse for them to be talking together. "Perhaps Mr. Davies has seen her," she added when he didn't reply. "If you'll excuse me...."

She gave a triumphant smile as Alex had no choice but to engage in conversation with the other man, the expression in his eyes warning her of the reprisals he would make the next time he saw her.

Their next meeting wasn't long in coming. Alex caught her up just outside the building, taking her elbow in a firm grip as he led her over to the car park.

"Let go of me, Alex." She tried to shake off his hand. "Daryl will be expecting me," she protested as he bundled her inside the newly mended Rolls-Royce.

"Then he can damn well wait," he snapped, coming round the car to get in beside her. He pulled her roughly into his arms. "This is your punishment for trying to avoid me." His head bent and his mouth claimed hers in a savage kiss.

It may have started out as a punishment, but it soon changed to the exchange of mutual passion. Lauri's arms were about his neck as she clung to him with her body and her lips.

Her face was flushed by the time Alex released her mouth, and she turned away in embarrassment. "Aren't you ever going to kiss me for any other reason but as a punishment?" she challenged, to hide her confusion.

"Yes." He pulled her toward him again, kissing her slowly, lingering over the possession of her mouth as if he wanted the caress to go on forever. Afterward he cradled her against his side, her head resting on his shoulder. "Better?" he asked huskily.

She nodded wordlessly, not even caring what she was doing anymore. This man made her mindless, completely devoid of any desire but to be with him, to be in his arms and be kissed by him.

"I meant to leave you alone until Saturday," he murmured into her hair. "But I found I had to see you again. I wanted to be with you last night, too, but I thought you would be with your boyfriend."

"I was," she confirmed.

His arm tightened painfully about her shoulders. "Did you sleep with him?" he demanded in a ragged voice.

"No!" Lauri struggled to pull out of his arms, but he refused to let her go.

"Have you ever slept with him?" he asked, his face grim, his expression the one of the cold, haughty stranger of their first meeting.

Lauri could never understand how he could always look so calm, so unmoved, after one of their passionate embraces, whereas she felt sure she must look a wreck, her hair in disorder from the wild caress of his hands, her eyes overbright, and her mouth red and throbbing from the hard pressure of his. That she thought he always looked calm seemed to imply that these onslaughts happened all the time, whereas she had in fact only known Alex three days. That he had kissed her every day of their acquaintance was beside the point; he had no right to do so and look so damned *normal* afterward, not when she felt as if she had been drawn down into a whirlpool.

"What my sleeping with Daryl has to do with you," she told him haughtily, "I have no idea."

His mouth tightened ominously. "It has a lot to do with me," he said tautly. "I want to know."

"What's the matter?" she taunted, stung by his arrogance. "Don't you like knowing who your predecessor was?"

"So you have slept with him." He removed his arm from about her shoulders, leaning forward to start the car engine. "I'm sure that's something else your Aunt Jane doesn't know about."

"Things as personal as that are no one's business but my own." She felt suddenly chilled without his closeness. "And I can never understand why they call it sleeping together. I'm sure what you do when you're awake has more importance than whether or not you sleep in the same bed."

Alex turned to quirk an eyebrow. "Don't you know?" he asked softly.

Lauri met that look almost shyly. "No," she shook her head.

His hand momentarily left the wheel to squeeze her fingers. "Thank you."

"For what?" She felt relief as they left the Blair office building far behind them.

"For not lying to me," he told her huskily.

"I've told enough lies to other people since meeting you; I have no intention of lying to you, too. Anyway, why should I lie about something like that?"

"You must know how I would have felt if you had said yes."

Her eyes widened questioningly. "I have no idea."

Alex turned to give her a considering look. "No, I don't suppose you do. I'm not sure I know myself; I just know that if you had slept with anyone I would want to kill him — slowly," he finished grimly.

"Alex!" she gasped.

He gave a rueful smile. "Primitive, isn't it? It's a new experience for me, so you'll have to bear with me. But I'm glad you're innocent, Lauren."

"I never said I was that," she said crossly, angry with him and yet not really sure why. She felt as if he were bull-dozing her into a relationship, forcing upon her a closeness to him that frightened the life out of her. She just wasn't up to his sophisticated games. "I think I was wrong to agree to go out with you. In fact, I didn't agree to it; you seduced me into it."

"As I'll seduce you again if you start being awkward. And talking of us going out together, I'm too old to be creeping about like this. I've never considered myself that reprehensible that women are ashamed to say they're going out with me."

"I'm not ashamed of it—"

"Thank God for that!" he mocked.

Lauri glared at him. "I'm not proud of it, either. If it became public knowledge I would have a terrible time once you've finished with me. I can just imagine the sympathetic looks I would get from your other employees when you stop dating me if they all knew about it. I'd have to leave my job, and I happen to like it."

"Wouldn't that be rather extreme?" He seemed to find it funny.

Her mouth set at his taunting. "You have obviously never heard the gossip that goes on around that place. I've only been there a few weeks, but I can see how someone's life can be made hell through thoughtless gossip. You should hear some of the things they say about—"

"Yes?" he prompted.

"Well, there's a lot of gossiping done in a place that size," she told him resentfully. "And Jane and Steve would come in for their share of it, too. They would make mincemeat out of the fact that you're dating your secretary's niece." She shuddered. "I can just imagine some of the things that would be said."

"So can I," he acknowledged dryly. "But I believe you were going to tell me some of the things said about me." He quirked an eyebrow.

"I wasn't going to tell you anything of the sort! But now that I've met you I'm sure most of the gossip is true. I bet you have had a hundred mistresses," she recounted with relish. "And I bet you did walk away from them all unscathed." This last was added with an ebbing of her self-confidence. No doubt he would walk away from her unscathed, too—and she wasn't sure she would be able to do the same.

"Hardly a hundred mistresses, Lauren," he said mockingly. "Maybe ninety-nine," he added with humor. "And I doubt I walked away from them all unscathed."

"One of them you didn't, anyway."

He frowned. "Which one?"

"The one that made you cynical," she explained. "The one that made you distrust the rest of us."

"I see," Alex laughed. "A little psychology. But it's wrong, I'm afraid, Lauren. It wasn't one, but all of those women that taught me those things."

She gulped. "*All* of them?"

He nodded. "They all wanted marriage, wanted a little lapdog of a man whom they could claim they had tamed. Isn't that what attracts women to men, the need to be the one who puts the ring through his nose, the collar and lead around his throat?"

"My God!" she spluttered with laughter. "What a conceited man you are! 'Ring through your nose' and 'collar and lead around your throat,'" she repeated disgustedly. "Any woman who wanted to tie herself to you for life would have to be insane. It isn't only men who are ensnared by marriage, you know; some women can feel that way about it, too."

"Do you?"

"Yes, I do!"

"That's because of your youth. Given a couple of years you'll be in the marriage market like all the rest."

"Stop the car!" she ordered furiously.

"What?" He blinked at her ferocity.

"I said stop the car!"

"What the hell for?"

"So that I can get out! You insulting, self-opinionated, supercilious—" she broke off her tirade as she saw he was laughing at her, openly chuckling at her remarks. "How

dare you!'' she exploded, her face fiery red, her eyes spar-
klingly green. "How dare you laugh at me! Stop this car,
you arrogant, rude, pig-headed—"

"Oh, Lauren." Still he laughed. "You're fantastic!"

Lauri frowned. "Fantastic?"

"Mmm," he smiled. "You've insulted me more in the
short time I've known you than anyone else has in the rest
of my life. I think you're adorable."

She blushed. "You won't get round me like that," she
told him sharply. "I don't react to that sort of flattery."

"No, I know what you react to."

"Your arrogance is beyond bearing! Are you going to
stop this car or not?" she demanded.

"Not."

"You—"

"No more names, Lauren. If you force me to stop the car
you know what the consequences will be."

"Consequences?"

"Don't you remember what happened the last time?"

"Oh." Color flooded her cheeks once again. "Yes. I—in
that case, *don't* stop the car."

She turned to stare stubbornly out of the window. She
didn't want any more reprisals like that. In fact, she didn't
even want to be here with him anymore. He made her say
things—things she didn't mean. She did feel that with the
wrong man marriage could be a trap, but with the right
man.... She dreamed of marriage like any other woman,
but this man made a mockery of even that.

"I'm sorry."

Lauri raised startled green eyes, searching his face for
some sign of that mockery—an apology was the last thing
she had been expecting from him. He looked perfectly serious. "For what?" she asked sulkily.

"For being—now what was it—insulting, self-opinionated, supercilious, arrogant, rude—"

"Don't say any more," she interrupted desperately. Had she really called him all those dreadful things? "You seem to have remembered what I said very well."

"I think so," he nodded. "I only missed off pig-headed, and that was because you didn't let me get that far. I'm sorry for being all of those things."

"That's all right," she said cheekily. "You can't help it."

His mouth quirked with humor. "I shall have to stop this car and kiss you in a minute."

"Don't you dare!"

"There's no satisfying you, is there?" He laughed, a deep husky sound that stirred the senses. "You're good for me, Lauren. You make me laugh; not many women can do that. Did you really mean it about thinking marriage a trap?"

"It can be," she evaded.

"Weren't your parents happy together?"

"Does there have to be a reason for my distrust?" she mocked. "Can't I just have decided it isn't for me?"

He shrugged. "It isn't normal in one your age."

"You mean I should be dreaming of white lace and orange blossom?" She mocked her own dreams before this hardened cynic did so. "As far as I can remember my parents were very happy together."

"As far as you can remember?" he asked interestedly.

He didn't miss much. "I was only seven when they died. Jane more or less brought me up."

"Did she bring Steve up, too?"

Lauri nodded. "Their own parents died years ago. Steve was fifteen when Jane took over, but it can't have been easy for her."

"Not if Steve was as much of a little devil at that age as I was," Alex agreed seriously. "I've always admired your aunt; now I have even more reason to do so. Are you the reason she's never married?"

She didn't take offense at the question; it was a normal conclusion to come to. "She says no—" Lauri shrugged "—but I'm not sure. Anyway, that could be changed in the near future. She has a steady boyfriend—sorry, *man* friend," she amended.

Alex's blue eyes narrowed. "And you think she might be going to marry him?"

She gave him a taunting look. "Worried you might lose your secretary?"

"Not at all," he returned smoothly. "I was just marveling at the secrets Jane keeps behind that cool facade. I've learned more about her the last three days than I did in the previous three years. Besides, if she left, you could always take her place."

Lauri shook her head. "My shorthand is lousy."

His smile was mocking. "I don't think I would care about that."

"And I don't think I would care for sitting on the boss's knee half the day," she retorted sharply. "That isn't the way I care to earn my money. Besides, I'm sure you would soon tire of my...inadequacies. You didn't get to be a successful businessman by having an idiot for a secretary."

"I think I could manage for a while," he said throatily, his gaze caressing.

"As I said, until you tire of me." She looked about her with a frown. "Where are we going, Alex? We've been driving for miles."

"Still worried about the boyfriend?"

She had forgotten all about poor Daryl! She would certainly have some explaining to do the next time she saw him. "Leave Daryl out of this," she told Alex tightly.

"I'd gladly forget about him altogether—if you would do the same thing."

"Well, I'm not going to. Now where are we going? I can't be late back twice in two days," she groaned.

"I'm afraid you are going to be late. In fact, you aren't going back at all today."

Lauri gasped. "Alex! I thought you were just taking me out to lunch!" she accused.

"I am taking you to lunch. I hope you don't mind eating at the airport."

Her mouth dropped open. "The airport? You mean Heathrow?"

"That's right. I'd take you somewhere else to eat, only we're a little late already."

Lauri turned right round in her seat to look at him. "We're going to *Heathrow*?"

"Mmm." He laughed as he looked at her. "Don't worry, Lauren, I don't intend whisking you off to some secret hideaway. We're going to meet someone."

"Who?" she asked dazedly.

"My brother-in-law," he told her calmly.

"You mean you're married?" she gasped. She had never heard of any marriage, but then that didn't mean there wasn't one. Jane didn't like talking about her employer's personal life, and she hadn't been with the company long enough herself to have heard all the gossip about him. Oh, God, she hadn't committed the unforgivable sin of going out with a married man, had she?

CHAPTER FIVE

ALEX GRINNED. "I would have thought by my views on marriage that you would know I'm not."

Her face was pale. "You could have those views because you *are* married."

He shook his head. "Laurence was married to my eldest sister, Beth."

She heaved an inward sigh of relief. "Surely you don't want me there when you meet a member of your family?"

"Actually, you'll be doing me a favor. Laurence and I haven't had a lot to do with each other for some time. We met for the first time in years six months ago at my sister's funeral."

"Oh, I'm sorry. I didn't realize she was dead."

"How could you; you didn't even know she existed." He was very serious now, his expression grim. "Beth had been an invalid for the last twenty years, confined to a wheelchair. I think she was glad to go," he added tautly.

"Oh, surely not! Alex, you can't mean that?" she said gently.

"But I do."

"But surely her husband—"

"Has not always been the paragon he should have been," Alex snapped. "But you don't want to hear my family history," he said briskly. "Laurence is returning to England to live after sixteen years of living in Switzerland. I may not agree with the way he conducted his marriage, but he is my brother-in-law, and I know Beth wouldn't like me to ignore him. He was a good father to their son."

Her eyes widened. "They have a child?"

"He was killed in the accident that left Beth crippled. There was no possibility of another child after the accident, not that I think their relationship was all that intimate before then. James was already five, and looking like being an only child. But Laurence was driving the car when James was killed and Beth was injured, and so he stayed with her."

The picture he painted wasn't a pleasant one—a man staying married to a woman he no longer loved because she was tied to a wheelchair, and their child dead through a mistake on his part. No, it wasn't pleasant at all, and it had obviously had an adverse effect on Alex, was probably part of the reason he was so bitter about marriage.

"I'm sorry," she said quietly.

"Don't be; I'm well over it now." He swung the Rolls into the car park. "But you can see why I'd be grateful for the presence of an unbiased third party."

"Yes," she nodded. Although she wasn't really sure she was unbiased; she couldn't help but see this from Alex's point of view. And she hadn't liked the implication that his brother-in-law had carried on affairs while his wife was confined to a wheelchair; it was somehow distasteful.

"Not that Laurence hasn't been the perfect husband for the past sixteen years," Alex instantly disabused her of that, almost as if he had read her thoughts. "But the damage had already been done. Nothing he could do could make up for the fact that he was once unfaithful to Beth."

"It's a long time to bear a grudge of that kind."

Alex turned to look at her after switching off the ignition.

"Would you forgive and forget if your husband had an affair?"

"I—I don't know. I thought we had just established that I don't ever want to get married," she reminded lightly.

He put out a hand to smooth one of her creamy cheeks. "We're two of a kind then," he murmured. "We should be good together, Lauren."

She moved away from that caressing hand. "I don't believe in affairs, either."

He raised a mocking eyebrow. "Do you intend remaining a virgin all your life?"

"No," she answered tautly. "I'm not a prude; when I find a man I can love I'll give myself freely to him. I've just got to meet a man I can love."

"And respect," he put in quietly.

"And respect."

"That means I'm already halfway there. We've already proven that you respect me," he drawled.

"I doubt I could love you," Lauri said distantly. "Shouldn't we be getting inside? Your brother-in-law's flight will be arriving shortly."

"I suppose so," he sighed. "Although I'm sure Laurence would wait."

As it happened the plane they were meeting had been delayed, and so they had time for lunch after all. Alex seemed preoccupied and Lauri left him to his dark thoughts, warned by the deep scowl on his face not to intrude.

At the time of the breakdown of his sister's marriage and accident he would have been about her age, very impressionable and very vulnerable. He had carried that disillusionment into adulthood, and she was sure it was the reason for his cynicism.

"Alex." She put her hand on his. "The flight arrival has just been called."

"Yes," he acknowledged tautly, a pulse beating erratically in his clenched jaw. He stood up. "Let's go."

He walked so fast she almost had to run to keep up with him, her legs being a lot shorter than his. A steady stream of people were leaving the arrival section, and Lauri knew straight away which man was Laurence Daniels. Alex reached out to grasp her hand painfully in his own as a tall, loose-limbed man in his late forties or early fifties came toward them; thick reddish brown hair with faint touches of gray, his face strong and lined, his eyes hidden beneath the tinted lenses of his glasses. He wore a casual linen suit and white silk shirt, a distinguished air about him.

"My God!" Alex groaned beside her, his face white, his mouth bloodless.

"What is it?" she demanded worriedly. "Alex, tell me what's wrong?"

"Nothing!" He looked at her coldly. "Nothing at all." He drew a ragged breath, dropping her hand to go forward and greet the other man.

Lauri stood in the background as the two men talked together for several minutes. Somehow this man didn't fit in with the description of a selfish man intent only on his own pleasure, and she found it hard to relate the cold facts that Alex had related to her with this man conversing so easily with the younger man. It didn't seem possible that this man was an adulterer; he just didn't seem the type. But was there a type? She didn't know.

Alex was bringing him over to meet her now, that cold look still in his eyes. "This is a friend of mine, Laurence," he said tauntingly. "Her name is Lauren," he told the other man slowly. "Lauren Prescott."

"Prescott?" Laurence Daniels echoed sharply, his face almost gray beneath his tan.

"Yes," Alex savagely bit the word out.

"Alex?" Lauri frowned. "Alex, what's wrong?"

"Nothing, my dear Lauren." His smile had a cruel edge to it. "Forgive me, I forgot to introduce you to my brother-in-law. Lauren, this is Laurence Daniels."

She put her hand out, smiling shyly. "Most people call me Lauri."

He returned her smile, taking her hand. "But not Alex," he said huskily.

"No, not Alex." Was it her imagination, or was Laurence Daniels holding on to her hand just a little too tightly... and for too long? Could Alex be right about him after all?

"I once knew some people called Prescott." Laurence Daniels's eyes never left her face, their expression shielded by the tinted glasses. "Your mother—"

"Is dead," she told him regretfully.

"Dead?" he repeated in a strangulated voice.

She nodded, surprised at the show of emotion he made no effort to hide. Even if he had known her family she could see no reason for her mother's death to have upset him so much; after all, they couldn't have been that friendly. "I'm afraid so," she confirmed.

"I see," he said heavily.

"Shouldn't you release her hand now, Laurence?" Alex put in coldly. "I'm sure she would like it back."

"Of course." Some of the color seemed to be ebbing back into the thin cheeks, although he was still very pale. And he would keep staring at her! It was very unnerving. "I'm sorry—Lauri." He gave a jerky smile.

"I—that's perfectly all right." But it wasn't! The intensity of his gaze was making her feel very uncomfortable.

"I'll just get my cases." He turned back to the trolley containing his luggage.

"Why does he keep staring like that?" Lauri whispered to Alex.

"Perhaps he finds you beautiful," he rasped, his face rigid.

"Don't be silly. We both know I'm not."

"Fishing for a compliment, my dear?" he taunted with a sneer.

She frowned. "I know you're tense about this meeting, Alex, but that's no reason for you to talk to me like this."

"Isn't it?" he scorned harshly. "My God, isn't it?"

"No. I—"

"Here we are." Laurence Daniels rejoined them. "Shall we go?"

"By all means, let's go." Alex led the way, striding off and leaving them to follow.

"I'm sorry about this," Lauri said awkwardly, falling into step beside Laurence Daniels, not really sure why she should have to apologize for Alex's disgraceful behavior. He was like a Dr. Jekyll and Mr. Hyde, and at the moment Mr. Hyde had definitely taken over.

Laurence shrugged. "I'm used to it." He watched her keenly. "Tell me, Lauri, have you known Alex long?"

She blushed. "Not very long, no."

"I wondered. You're very young to be one of his girl friends."

"Eighteen isn't all that young nowadays," she told him defensively.

"Eighteen…" he echoed huskily. "Yes, I suppose you would be. And you have no father to help advise you."

It was a statement, not a question, and Lauri frowned. This was the strangest conversation! But then Laurence Daniels seemed to be a strange man. He seemed quite nice, and yet there was still the way he kept staring at her, and if he were a younger man she would suspect that look. But surely a man of his age couldn't be interested in the girl she still was? No, she was sure he wasn't. Maybe he was trying to see Alex's interest in her. She was curious as to the conclusion he came to, especially as she didn't have one herself.

"No, I have no father," she confirmed.

"I'm sure if you had, he would advise you Alex is a very dangerous man."

"Dangerous?" she repeated disbelievingly. "Surely that's too strong a word, Mr. Daniels?" Although the savage cruelty in his face minutes earlier had given her some hint of the side of his character he usually held in check.

"Call me Laurence," the man at her side invited. "And I think dangerous is quite a mild word to describe Alex." He looked at his brother-in-law's rigid back as he walked ten or fifteen yards in front of them. "Much too mild," he murmured almost to himself.

Lauri automatically got in the back of the Rolls, leaving the seat next to Alex for Laurence Daniels, feeling slightly piqued when Alex didn't even seem to notice she was there, let alone where she sat. She could excuse his behavior if it was just directed at his brother-in-law, but she didn't understand why she was being included in the cold-shoulder treatment.

"Lauri has just been telling me that you haven't known each other long," Laurence spoke to Alex.

Alex's attention remained rigidly fixed on the road in front of them as he drove the car with his usual skill. "No, not very long," he agreed tautly.

"Where did you find her?" Laurence probed.

He was given a cold angry stare. "Find her?" Alex snapped. "Isn't that a strange way of putting it?" he scorned.

"Is it?" Laurence appeared unmoved by the other man's terse manner.

"I work for your brother-in-law, Mr. Daniels," Lauri put in to ease the tension. "In the typing pool."

"I see," he nodded.

"Do you, Laurence?" Alex rasped, shaking his head. "I doubt it. I doubt it very much."

"Oh, I think I do," Laurence disagreed. "I'm just wondering if you're ever going to forget the past, Alex," he said almost wearily.

Alex gave him a glacial look. "I think today has made that impossible, don't you?"

"This isn't the past, Alex," he was told. "This is the future."

"Do you think there is a future there? Isn't it just a little too late?"

"I'm hoping not."

"I wish you luck," Alex said bitterly.

"I wish you meant that," Laurence sighed. "Maybe I'm too old to be thinking of starting again."

"Maybe you won't get the chance," Alex told him tautly.

"I'm not expecting it to be easy." The first show of impatience entered the other man's voice.

"It won't be," Alex said with satisfaction. "And at least you won't be getting all that you wanted."

"No." Laurence Daniels seemed to go gray again. "No, I won't, will I?"

"You weren't expecting that, were you? It wasn't the way you had things planned at all."

"I didn't plan anything, Alex. And I certainly didn't expect to be able to come back here as if I'd never been away. But now I have a bonus I didn't even know about. I don't mean to let that pass me by."

"You can't honestly tell me that you didn't know?" Alex's disbelief bordered on sarcasm.

"Do you think if I had that things would have been as they were?" Laurence demanded fiercely. "I may be a fool, but I'm not a masochist."

Lauri sat on the back seat trying to ignore their heated conversation—or argument, to give it its proper definition. That Alex was to blame for it she had no doubt, and it was really too bad of him to act like this in front of her.

When the Rolls drew up outside her house she got out with unconcealed haste, taking her leave of a smiling Laurence Daniels and a rigid-faced Alex. He was like a stranger, a cold silent stranger who suddenly seemed to hate her.

"I'll okay things with Carly," he bit out. "About this afternoon," he explained.

She frowned her puzzlement over his behavior to her. "It doesn't matter. I'll talk to her myself. Goodbye, Mr. Daniels. It was nice meeting you."

"I'm sure we'll meet again, my dear." He got out of the car to stand on the pavement beside her, looking up at the house she had called home all of her life.

"Not with me you won't," Alex put in grimly.

"Nevertheless, I'm sure Lauri and I will meet again," Laurence Daniels said firmly. He looked back at the house. "Did your mother live here, too?"

Lauri frowned. "Yes. Did you—did you know my mother?"

He gave a rather sad smile. "I believe I did, yes."

"My father, too?"

"I, er, I may have done."

"Can we go now, Laurence?" Alex interrupted tersely. "I do have other commitments. I'm meeting Connie in half an hour, and she isn't a lady who likes to be kept waiting."

"Connie?" Laurence frowned, looking at Lauri. "But I thought . . . ."

Lauri forced a rather strained smile, sure that Alex had made that remark about Connie Mears as a deliberate ploy to hurt her. "Alex and I are only friends, Mr. Daniels." Not even that now! "I already have a boyfriend."

"You do?"

"Oh, yes." She nodded, smiling brightly.

"I didn't realize that."

"There was no reason why you should. Goodbye, Mr. Daniels. Alex." She almost ran into the house, anxious to escape from the kind query she could see in the older man's face.

She had hardly had time to close the front door before Jane came rushing out into the hallway, a strangely ruffled Jane who looked more than slightly agitated.

"Where have you been?" she demanded without preamble.

"Where have I been?" Lauri frowned. "Where do you think I've been?"

"Well, you haven't been at work, I know that," Jane said impatiently.

"How do you know that?" she delayed.

"What does it matter how I know!"

"Well, I—"

"Carly told me. She wanted to know if you were ill. She said something about you not seeming yourself this morning. When you didn't go back after lunch she became concerned and called me. Naturally I telephoned here, and when I got no answer I decided to come home and check that you hadn't collapsed or something. Mr. Blair wasn't in this afternoon, so at least I didn't have to explain to him that my niece had done a disappearing act and I had to go and look for her."

Lauri took off her jacket, turning to hang it up to give herself time to collect her thoughts. "I didn't think my taking the afternoon off would cause such a fuss," she said lightly. "I suppose that's what comes of working in the same place as the rest of my family."

Jane's brown eyes widened. "Are you telling me that you just took the afternoon off?"

"Well—"

"You just decided not to go back?" Jane demanded that she answer.

"It wasn't quite like that—"

"I'd be interested to hear what it was like! It was because Steve and I already worked at Blair's that you found it so easy to get this job. And now you've abused that connection by taking time off on a *whim*," her voice rose angrily. "You aren't still at school, you know. You can't just take time off when you feel like it."

"I realize that."

"I'm glad to hear it. You're still in your month's trial, so I hope you can find a reasonable excuse to give Carly."

"I'll think of something," she evaded.

"Then I hope it's something good," Jane snapped, "because she's been as worried as I have."

Lauri bowed her head. "I'm sorry." It wasn't often that her aunt lost her temper, but when she did it was something to take notice of.

"Don't say sorry to me," Jane dismissed. "It's Carly you should be apologizing to. Needless to say, I'm very disappointed in you."

"Does Steve know about this, too?" After his suspicions of yesterday he just might put two and two together and come up with the right answer!

"No." Luckily Jane didn't hear her sigh of relief. "And

I'm not going to tell him,'' Jane further put her mind at rest. "I don't see why both of us should be upset by your thoughtlessness. You could have been lying dead in a ditch, for all we knew," she added angrily.

"I've said I'm sorry." Lauri looked at her pleadingly. "It won't happen again."

"It had better not," Jane warned. "Carly seemed to be under the impression you were having dental treatment and that perhaps you weren't feeling well after it. This time off hasn't happened before, has it?" she asked suspiciously.

"No." She shook her head vigorously. After all, she had only been a little bit late back yesterday.

"Then make sure it doesn't happen again."

"I will."

It seemed that her arguments weren't over for the day. Daryl was in a terrible mood when he arrived to take her out later that evening.

"Where were you at lunchtime?" he demanded angrily, pushing past her to enter the house.

Lauri sighed, knowing she was in for another time of questioning. And all because of a man who seemed to have calmly dismissed her from his life. She wished she could do the same to him. Alex had changed in his attitude toward her some time during the afternoon, and telling her he was meeting Connie Mears had been a deliberate attempt to hurt her.

And it had hurt her, more than she cared to admit. She had thought herself to merely be attracted to him, a mindless attraction that would die as quickly as it had flamed into life. But the thought of him with another woman made her burn with jealousy.

If only she knew what she had done to make him suddenly change toward her. If she could pinpoint when it had happened— She frowned. It had happened as soon as they had met Laurence Daniels at the airport. Until then everything had been normal between them. She knew Laurence Daniels had held her hand too long, that he had kept staring at her, but surely Alex's attitude couldn't be due to *jealousy* of his brother-in-law? It didn't seem possible that Alex could imagine meeting Laurence Daniels had meant anything to her, pleasant as he may have seemed, and yet she could think of no other explanation.

"Lauri!" Daryl cut into her thoughts impatiently. "You aren't even listening to me!" he accused.

She bit her lip. "Sorry. I—I was miles away."

"That's obvious," he scowled.

"Daryl—"

"Were you also miles away at lunchtime too, when you should have been meeting me?" he cut in forcefully.

She quite literally had been, although she couldn't tell him that! "I—I wasn't feeling well," she lied. "I left early."

"So I gathered when I went to your office to see you. The only trouble is," he added slowly, "there's a rumor going around that you left with Alexander Blair."

Lauri paled, her eyes huge green lakes of despair. "Who told you that?" she croaked breathlessly.

"Does it matter?" he shrugged. "Surely all that matters is whether or not it's true."

She forced a careless laugh. "Of course it isn't," she dismissed tautly. "How on earth do rumors like that start?"

Daryl's eyes were narrowed as they searched her features. "They usually start with a grain of truth."

"Do they?" Her voice was slightly shrill. "Oh, well, I can't— Oh, I know. Maybe Mr. Davies saw me talking to Mr. Blair before lunch and assumed we were together. Yes, that must be it," she announced almost triumphantly.

Some of Daryl's anger began to fade, and he eyed her uncertainly. "Do you think that's it?"

"It must be, mustn't it?" she reasoned. "I can't think of any other way such a story could have started. Mr. Blair was just asking me if I had seen Jane, that was all."

Still Daryl frowned. "Bob Davies has never seemed the gossipy type to me."

"No? Well, I—I don't suppose he is. But his wife could be. She does work in accounts, too. Maybe he mentioned it to her and then she mentioned it to someone else, so that by the time it reached you they had me going out with the man. You know how quickly these things become distorted."

"I suppose so," he agreed slowly.

Lauri laughed. "You don't honestly think I had lunch with Alexander Blair, do you?"

"I—no." He gave a sheepish grin.

She heaved an inward sigh of relief. All she needed now was for Steve to challenge her and she could have a complete set. But luckily her uncle hadn't been in the office at all today, and he hadn't got in from his rounds until after Jane had left the house—although she might not escape questioning from him when he had been in to work and been acquainted with the gossip about his niece.

How *had* that story got around, and so quickly, too! It may have happened the way she had described to Daryl, although it was more likely that someone had seen Alex kissing her in his parked car; after all, the Blair building did overlook that car park. So all her efforts to keep their meetings a secret had been a waste of time. And it could all have been for nothing anyway. The way Alex had behaved when they parted earlier, she didn't think there would be any meetings to be kept secret in future.

"Shall we stop discussing boring old Alex Blair and go out?" She gave Daryl her most endearing smile.

"You're feeling better, then?" The scowl hadn't left him.

"Better? Oh, yes, yes, I feel fine now. Are we going out?"

He sighed. "I suppose so."

But he wasn't very good company, and she couldn't really blame him. She hadn't been fair to him the last few days, and so she deserved his moody behavior. She had no excuse for the way she had been behaving, except perhaps that she found Alex Blair so overwhelming. But that wasn't really a good excuse, and she ought to be thoroughly ashamed of herself. Looked at coldly, it would seem as if she had gone after a better prospect, although she herself knew she had simply been rushed off her feet by an Alex who wouldn't be denied.

The girls in her office suddenly went silent when she got in the next morning, and if they had heard the same gossip Daryl had, it wasn't surprising. What made it worse was that she hadn't been with the company very long, wasn't particularly friendly with any of the other girls in the typing pool, and so she found it all the more awkward to behave as if everything was as normal.

By the time coffee break came around, she was beginning to feel really uncomfortable, wishing she could just walk out and never come back. But she had always been a fighter, and she wouldn't be seen to run away from anything.

She didn't bother to go to the canteen with the others, opting to stay behind and finish off some of the work she had been constantly making mistakes in all morning. Besides, she was grateful for the breather from curious looks and unasked questions.

"Are they giving you a hard time?"

She looked up to find Carly standing in front of her desk. She shrugged. "They're curious, that's all."

"Aren't we all?" Carly grinned.

She had accepted Lauri's excuse that just talking about going to the dentist, had made her feel ill, although she had told her to call in the next time.

Lauri couldn't look at her now. "You've heard the rumors?"

She nodded. "Like everyone else."

"Not everyone," Lauri denied. "My aunt and uncle haven't heard them yet, although it can only be a matter of time."

But it seemed her luck was in, or it could just have been that people were just too polite to actually speak to Jane and Steve about their niece. Whatever the reason, they seemed to know nothing about the fact that she had been rumored to be dating their employer.

And she had heard nothing from Alex. By Friday afternoon she was tired of waiting to know if their date for tomorrow was on or off, so tired of waiting she decided to call him and find out for herself. This time she chose to use one of the public telephones in the building, waiting until their afternoon break before leaving the girls who were still a little strained with her, although the sensation surrounding her seemed to be fading, probably due to her own air of innocence about the matter.

Jane answered the telephone, and once again Lauri adopted the sexy voice as she asked for Alex. By the long wait she had, she knew that at least Alex was in his office. Besides, if he hadn't been, Jane would have said so at the onset.

"Miss, er, Lauren?" Jane came back on the telephone.

"Yes?" she asked in that breathless voice.

"I'm afraid Mr. Blair is unable to talk to you at the moment. He's in an important meeting," she added.

So she had her answer; Alex didn't even want to speak to her. "Thank you," she said huskily.

"Perhaps you could call back later?"

Lauri could almost hear the sympathy in her aunt's voice, and she cringed in reaction. Jane had never mentioned having to give Alex Blair's girl friends the brush-off, but it was natural to assume this wasn't the first time it had happened. Well, she had her pride, and she had no intention of telephoning Alex only to be put off again.

"No, that's perfectly all right," she said lightly. "Thank you."

"Oh, but . . . Lauren? I—Mr. Blair—"

Lauri slowly put down the receiver. Poor Jane; how embarrassing for her to have to do Alex's dirty work for him. Still, at least she knew where she stood now. She could begin to forget she had ever known Alexander Blair as anything other than an employer.

Her date with Daryl was a success that evening, managing to get back on the friendly level they had always been, making their final goodbye the next day all the sadder. She went with him to the airport, finding it hard to think she would never see him again. They had had fun together the last few weeks, even if she had stupidly got sidetracked by Alex Blair's charm.

"Are you going out tonight?" Steve put the newspaper down after taking down the football results, sighing as he knew that once again he hadn't won on his coupon.

"Are you?" she returned.

He grinned. "I asked first."

She shrugged. "I have nowhere to go."

"Upset about Daryl leaving?" he asked gently.

"A bit," she nodded.

"Feel like coming out with me tonight?"

"With you?" Her eyes widened.

Steve laughed at her expression. "Don't look so surprised. I realize I'm your uncle, and therefore considered unsuitable for spending an evening out with, but there's no law against it. Honest!"

"I know that," she smiled. "I just didn't expect—" She sighed. "I don't really think I'm in the mood." Not when she should have been going out with Alex! "Although I do appreciate the offer," she added gently.

"Sure?"

"Mmm. But thanks."

He shrugged. "Okay. But you aren't going to pine away for him, are you?"

Lauri laughed. "Haven't you heard we don't do that sort of thing anymore? But I do thank you for offering. It was a nice thought, Steve."

He stood up. "I'll be leaving about seven-thirty if you should change your mind."

She nodded. "Okay."

But she knew she wouldn't be going. Parting from Daryl had been upsetting, yes, but knowing she should have been with Alex tonight was what made everything so depressing.

"You're looking nice," she told Jane as she came into the room at eight o'clock, Steve having already left.

"Don't I usually?" Jane teased.

"You know you do," Lauri smiled.

Jane grimaced. "I hope so. This weekend with Robin's parents is important to me. I have to try to make a good impression, although I must say it seems a little strange at my age."

Lauri laughed. "I wouldn't like it at any age." Especially if Robin's parents were anything like him! "So you really do like Robin?" she probed.

Her aunt shrugged. "He's steady...and reliable," she added almost bitterly. "Not too many men can be called that nowadays."

She had never heard Jane talk this way before...and it worried her. "But do you love him?"

"I—" She broke off as the doorbell rang. "That will be him now. When you get to my age, Lauri, you look for more than just love. You become a little more concerned about other aspects of their personality. Robin will never let me down."

"But—"

"I have to let him in, Lauri. One day you'll know what I mean," Jane told her dully.

Lauri's worried gaze followed her aunt out of the room. Jane couldn't marry Robin just because he was steady, reliable and would never let her down! It was no basis for marriage, and she did so want her aunt to be happy.

She sat hunched over her knees in the chair, her denims old and faded, her jumper thin and fitting tautly over her breasts, staring aimlessly into space.

"Lauri...."

"Mmm?" She looked up at the sound of Jane's voice, her eyes widening, her face going pale as she saw the man who stood next to her aunt.

"Lauri—" Jane was obviously having difficulty articulating "—Mr. Blair says the two of you have a dinner date this evening."

CHAPTER SIX

LAURI STOOD UP. "Alex...."

"Lauren." He nodded distantly, very attractive in white dinner jacket, black trousers and snowy white silk shirt.

"Lauren?" Jane echoed sharply. " *You're* Lauren?" She looked accusingly at her niece.

Lauri gulped, not understanding any of this. "But I— Yesterday Jane said you were in a meeting and couldn't talk to me, and I—I—"

"I was in a meeting," Alex informed her calmly. "And it certainly wasn't the type of meeting where I could carry on a telephone conversation with you."

"But I—"

"Lauri?" Jane curtly interrupted. "Are you telling me that you are the Lauren who has been telephoning Al—er— Mr. Blair?"

"Alex will do, Jane," he told her deeply, the coldness of his blue eyes momentarily lightened with humor. "That is what you call me in the privacy of the office."

She gave him a look of deep irritation. "Lauri?" she prompted sharply. "Will you kindly tell me what's going on?"

How could she when she didn't know herself? Alex being here tonight was as much of a shock to her as it was to Jane. And in spite of his unexpected appearance here, he didn't look any more friendly than he had at their last parting.

Jane shook her head dazedly. "I—Mr. Blair—"

"It's quite simple, Jane," he interrupted patiently. "Lauren and I do have a date for this evening, but for some reason Lauren seems to have forgotten all about it."

Lauri's eyes flashed as she glared at him. "I didn't forget," she snapped.

He shrugged. "Changed your mind then. But if that were the case you should have let me know."

"I didn't change my mind, either! *You* were the one who did that," she accused.

"*I* did?" he challenged haughtily. "And just when did I do that?"

"You know when," she mumbled, unable to look at him.

"Would someone please explain this to me?" Jane sounded at the end of her patience. "Have I understood this correctly—have you taken Lauri out before?" she demanded of her boss.

"I have," he confirmed. "A couple of times."

Jane looked at her niece. "Lauri?"

She looked up with apprehensive eyes. "Yes?"

"Why didn't you tell me?"

"Because I—I— You came here deliberately to cause trouble!" she rounded on Alex Blair. "Admit it," she said fiercely.

"Lauri!" Jane looked scandalized. "Remember who you're talking to."

"Oh, I remember." Green eyes flashed. "And I'll remember this, too, Mr. High-and-mighty Blair." Her explosive temper was in full flow. "You knew damned well I didn't want people to know I was meeting you, and yet you've gone out of your way to make sure people do know."

"And how have I done that?" He eyed her with narrowed blue eyes.

"By kissing me in the car park in full view of anyone looking out of the window, by—"

"I don't remember you objecting at the time," he drawled. "In fact, I believe you asked for more of the same."

"You conceited swi—"

"Lauri!" Once again her aunt cut in. "Don't add to the seriousness of this situation by insulting Mr. Blair."

"Why shouldn't I, if he deserves it?" she returned resentfully. "And believe me, he deserves it."

"I'm not sure I'll ever believe what you tell me again," Jane said dully. "You seem to have told me one lie on top of another. You weren't ill Wednesday afternoon, were you? You were with Mr. Blair."

"I—"

"Weren't you?" Jane demanded she answer truthfully.

"Yes, I was. But I didn't intend to be. He more or less kidnapped me."

"Don't be ridiculous," Jane snapped.

"But he did," she protested.

"And was it on the occasion of this 'kidnapping' that he kissed you in the car park?"

Lauri blushed. "Well, he—I—"

"Was it?"

"Yes," she admitted miserably.

"I can't believe this." Her aunt shook her head. "It's too incredible to be taken in."

"There's nothing incredible about it, Jane," Alex told her calmly. "Your niece and I are attracted to each other and so we're going out together. There's nothing incredible about that."

"You keep out of this!" Lauri turned on him angrily. "You came here tonight with the intention of causing a scene like this."

"I came here tonight because you were supposed to have met me at eight o'clock. When you didn't turn up, it was logical to come to your home."

His calm explanation only infuriated her more. "You know why I didn't turn up," she told him almost accusingly. "I haven't seen you since Wednesday, not since you mentioned having to see your girl friend."

"I seem to remember you saying you were seeing your boyfriend, too," he reminded. "But I still turned up for *our* arranged date this evening."

"So would I have done if I'd known it was still on. Why do you think I called you yesterday? You knew I'd telephoned, and yet you didn't bother to call me back."

He shrugged. "I was late getting out of the meeting, and I didn't think you would appreciate my calling you at home."

"So instead you chose to come here now and cause trouble!"

"Not at all. I've already explained my reasons. And I'm sure your aunt can't be interested in our petty squabbles. If you'll just go and change we can be on our way."

"Go to hell! If you think I—"

"Lauri!" If anything Jane was even more shocked. "Just learn to control that temper of yours. I've warned you about it often enough. But first you can apologize to Mr. Blair."

Her eyes flashed her dislike of him. "I will not! He started this. He—"

"You *will* apologize," Jane's voice was steely. "And right now."

Lauri looked from Jane's set face to Alex Blair's bland one. She sensed the mockery behind that expression, and her hands clenched into fists as she only just stopped herself from hitting him. But Jane's tone brooked no argument. "I'm sorry," she muttered resentfully. "But you—"

"Don't ruin it by being insulting again— Oh, damn," Jane cursed as the doorbell rang. "This time it has to be Robin," she said absently.

"Robin?" Alex quirked an eyebrow. "Oh, yes, the boyfriend you're serious about."

Jane blushed. "I wouldn't go that far. But we are quite close, yes."

"So Lauren told me."

"Did she indeed?" Jane's mouth was tight. "And what else has she told you about us?"

He shrugged. "Not a lot. I think you should answer the door," he advised as the bell rang again. "He seems to be getting impatient."

"You trouble-making swine!" Lauren flared once she was alone with him.

He sat down, completely unperturbed by her anger. "More names, Lauren?" he mused. "Are you asking for the punishment, I wonder?"

Remembering what form his punishment always took, she moved a safe distance away from him. "Keep your kisses to yourself," she said tautly. "Why did you come here? Why?"

"I thought I had just explained all that," he said with a sigh. "I gave you fifteen minutes to turn up, Lauren."

"You must have known that after Wednesday I wouldn't be there."

"Wednesday?" he frowned. "What happened Wednesday to change anything?"

"You were nasty to me," she reminded.

"I thought you understood about that. The meeting with Laurence turned out to be much more...traumatic than I had thought it would be."

"I could see that," her voice softened. "But I didn't see

that it was necessary for me to receive the same treatment as he did.''

"No," he agreed huskily, his eyes piercing as they never wavered from her face. "You're right," he sighed. "And I'm sorry."

Only the second time he had ever apologized to her, it once again rendered her speechless. She frowned. He was making all the right moves, saying all the right things, and yet underneath all that there was a contemptuous look in his eyes, a bitter twist to his mouth. She didn't trust him, and she daren't let herself trust anything he was saying.

"That's perfectly all right," her voice was stilted. "Now, if that's all, I intend spending a quiet evening at home."

"Suits me." He shrugged, the contempt in his eyes now replaced by a much warmer emotion. "I could do with a...quiet evening, at home, too."

She deliberately ignored the sensuous curve to his mouth, the explosion of passion in suddenly brilliant blue eyes. "Then I hope you enjoy it. I believe *your* home is in Mayfair," she added sweetly.

Alex gave a husky laugh, settling more comfortably into the armchair he occupied. "Sorry, Lauren, I can't oblige," he taunted. "I'm not going anywhere."

Her mouth set in a stubborn line. "But I don't want you here!"

"Tell me that again once we're alone, completely alone," he said in a bored voice. "But give me five minutes or so before you do."

Lauri blushed, well aware of what he intended taking place in that five minutes. She was also aware that five minutes in his arms could reduce her to his sexual slave. "I'd rather you left now," she told him tautly.

"I'll bet you would," he grinned. "Would you like me to

come over there now and change your mind for you? Jane and her boyfriend might find it embarrassing when they come in, but then, so could you."

"But not you!" she scorned. "I'm sure my aunt is quite used to entering a room and finding you in a passionate embrace with some female or other."

His eyes narrowed. "Meaning?"

"Meaning that although my aunt is too loyal ever to say so, I'm sure you often entertain your women friends in your office."

To her chagrin he smiled. "I don't think there would be much there to entertain them—unless you count me, of course," he added tauntingly.

"I don't," she snapped.

"You don't find me... entertaining?" He quirked one eyebrow mockingly.

How could she have ever thought this man attractive and charming? He was absolutely hateful! "I'd give you five out of ten," she drawled insultingly.

"Really?" He stood up with some force, a dangerous glitter in his eyes, his mouth a taut angry line. "Against who?" he ground out.

Lauri shrugged nonchalantly. "Against any of the other men I've known." She knew she was deliberately baiting him, and yet she couldn't help herself.

"Against Daryl?"

She knew she was inviting his anger down upon her, but she was so angry herself that she didn't care anymore. "Of course," she derided.

"My God, you asked for this!" He pulled her effortlessly into his arms, molding her savagely against the hard contours of his body, knowing he was hurting her and yet not giving a damn. His mouth ground down on hers with a fierceness that took her breath away, forcing her lips apart so that his tongue could deepen the kiss.

He didn't even need the allotted five minutes to reduce her to a pliant, eager body in his arms. She quivered as he took possession of her breasts beneath her jumper. She had never felt like this before, never wanted, with a desperation that bordered on madness, the feel of a man's lips on her body. And not just any man—it had to be Alex Blair.

His breathing was ragged when he at last lifted his head, his face white with the hard tension she could feel in his body. "Well?" he challenged, not relinquishing his hold on her.

"Perhaps I miscalculated." He was just as unmoved as usual! She played with the buttons of his shirt, releasing two of them to slip her hand inside, instantly feeling the erratic beat of his heart, the shallowness of his breathing. "I think you merit at least—oh, five and a half," she finished disdainfully, throwing her head back to meet the fierce anger in his face head on.

The last defiant gesture was her undoing, giving Alex easy access to her parted lips, allowing him to grind her lips against her teeth. She began to struggle in earnest as his fingers bit painfully into the tenderness of her breasts.

Her own hand clenched into a claw inside his shirt as he refused to let her go, and she raked her nails down his bare chest. He instantly moved back with a cry of pain, and as he did so Lauri could see blood beginning to stain the whiteness of his shirt, four red streaks that quickly soaked a trail down his chest.

"You little vixen!" he swore angrily, his face contorted with rage and pain. "You vicious little bitch!"

Lauri straightened her own clothing, her face pale with the shock of what she had done. But Alex didn't induce any half-hearted emotions within her; he evoked either love or hate, both equally as strong as the other, and at the moment she had hated him.

But *love*! Her face paled even more. She couldn't love this man! How could she have used such a term toward him even in her thoughts? What she felt for Jane and Steve was love, and that was nothing like the destructive emotions she felt toward Alex. He angered her, aroused her, but that couldn't be called *love*. Could it?

"... and so you see, Robin, I'll just have to cancel this weekend." Jane and Robin entered the lounge, neither of them seeming to notice the rapid rise and fall of Lauri's breasts as she tried to bring some order to her chaotic thoughts, or to notice the way Alex turned away, pulling his jacket over the unmistakable streaks of blood on his shirt.

"But what do I tell my parents?" Robin complained, his good-looking face creased into a frown.

At thirty-eight Robin was a very successful lawyer, tall and handsome, with a taste for subdued clothing—usually dark gray or navy-blue suits—and a way of assessing everyone by their bank account. A look of respect entered his eyes as he looked at Alexander Blair, quickly replaced by irritation as his gaze passed on to Lauri.

Jane sighed. "I've already explained that I can't possibly go away and leave Lauri now."

"And I've already said that I can't understand why you should concern yourself with whom your niece chooses to go out with," he returned impatiently. "I'm sure Mr. Blair is respectable."

"Thank you." Alex bowed mockingly.

Lauri was amazed at how quickly he had managed to get himself under control, no evidence now of his burning anger of a few minutes ago, while she still felt emotionally shattered, her hands shaking as she pushed back her cloud of red gold hair.

"I didn't mean any offense," Robin said hastily, making Lauri cringe at his fawning attitude. How Jane could stand such a man she had no idea. He may be as she described, steady and reliable, but he was also boring, and his deferential manner toward Alex made her feel sick.

"None taken," Alex replied smoothly. "And there's really no need for you to cancel your weekend away because of Lauren and myself. We've just decided we aren't going out after all."

"You have?" Jane sounded relieved.

"Mmm." He nodded. "We've decided to stay here instead."

Lauri gave him a sharp look, wondering if anyone else could see that dangerous glitter in his eyes. The retribution that look promised made her determined *not* to stay here. "I've decided I would like to go out after all," she said shakily. "If you have no objections?"

"None." Revenge would be his wherever they were, his eyes told her. "Unless you and your boyfriend intend coming with us," he spoke to Jane, "I suggest you carry on with your plans to meet Robin's parents."

"Yes, darling," Robin encouraged. "It's too late to call them now and say we aren't going."

"But I—"

"I'm only taking Lauren to dinner," Alex soothed. "And then I'll bring her straight back. I'm sure Steve will be a very good chaperon."

"Well...."

"Oh, do hurry, Jane." Robin looked impatiently at his wristwatch. "I told them we would be there by ten."

Jane sighed. "I don't know why we couldn't have just

gone down tomorrow. Ten o'clock is hardly a decent time to arrive.''

''You know I had work to do today, and this way we'll have all of tomorrow with my parents. You have to give them some time to get to know you. Now do hurry up,'' Robin ordered impatiently.

''Will you be all right?'' Jane asked Lauri.

No, she wouldn't, not by the looks Alex was giving her! But she couldn't let her own fear interfere with Jane's plans. ''Of course I will,'' she smiled brightly. ''Go and get your overnight case.''

The other couple finally left, and Lauri turned apprehensively to face Alex. His expression told her nothing now, his features once again bland. Lauri's hands twisted nervously together in front of her, a show of her inner agitation.

''So that's Robin,'' he mused softly.

His first remark was far from what she had expected. ''You didn't like him.'' It was a statement, not a question.

''I hardly had the chance to make that sort of decision,'' he mocked. ''I do know that if I had a girl like Jane interested enough to marry me, I wouldn't give a damn how my parents felt about her.''

''You like Jane?'' She swallowed hard.

''Very much. Don't you?''

Her eyes flashed. ''It's hardly the same thing.''

His mouth twisted mockingly. ''I like Jane because she's genuine and honest. She has no hidden depths. She's a very lovely woman.'' His tone implied *she* was the opposite.

''Yes,'' Lauri agreed huskily, still waiting for retribution for those scratches. They must be very sore by now.

''Go and change, Lauren,'' he told her almost wearily. ''Before I change my mind and decide to stay here after all.''

Her eyes widened. "You really are going to take me out?"

"Yes," he said grimly, pulling back his jacket to look at the bloodstain. "In spite of this," he grimaced.

It did look bad. How could she have done such a thing? Her throbbing breasts answered that question for her. She moved forward, her hand outstretched. "Let me—"

"No!" He jerked away from her. "I think you've done enough."

"But I was only going to suggest I wash your chest and put some antiseptic on it."

"That won't be necessary," he told her coldly. "It isn't important."

"But it looks a mess!"

"And no doubt it is," he said grimly. "But you should have thought of that before you chose to use your talons on me. I can see to it later," he dismissed.

"But—"

"Do you want to stay here?" The question was a threat.

"No!" She almost ran out of the room, his mocking laughter following her up the stairs.

She had a quick shower, quick because she didn't trust him not to come up here and finish what they had started. Her wardrobe was pretty limited, especially for an evening with Alexander Blair. She had intended buying a new gown, but when the date seemed to be off, hadn't bothered. She finally chose to wear the only gown that was in the least sophisticated.

She had first worn the gown when she was a bridesmaid the previous year. The bride had chosen to put her bridesmaids in white while she herself wore black. It had been an odd sort of wedding altogether, the bridegroom wearing white, too, and Lauri hadn't been altogether surprised when the marriage had broken up after only a few weeks. Both Iris and Nicky had seemed more interested in causing a sensation at the wedding, which their extraordinary outfits had certainly done, than in the actual marriage that followed.

But at least Lauri had the white gown out of it, a beautiful floaty affair, with thin ribbon shoulder straps, a fitted bodice, flowing gently from the waist to her ankles. She turned in panic as the door clicked open behind her. Alex stood in the open doorway. She clutched at the open back of her gown, her face fiery red at his insolent appraisal.

"Very nice," he finally taunted. "Having a little trouble?" he mocked her efforts to pull up the zip.

"Oh, go away!" Her face was flushed with her efforts, realizing that the zip had actually caught on a bit of the material.

He did the opposite, coming forward to spin her around, bending to look at the mess she was making of her gown. "Hold still," he commanded as she began to fidget.

How was she supposed to do that with his fingers touching her bare skin! Her teeth set in a grimace as he seemed to deliberately linger over the task, his hands seeming to burn where they touched. He must be aware of how she was trembling, couldn't miss the way she longed to move sensuously against his fingers splayed across her back.

"There." He pulled the zip up to the top with no trouble at all, his hands resting possessively on her hips as he spun her around to face him. "Ready now?" he asked huskily.

"I—I just have to brush my hair."

"I'll see you downstairs."

To say she was dazed by his behavior was putting it mildly. But his manner remained coolly polite as he opened the car door for her, making her wonder if that brutal assault of earlier had really happened. But of course it had.

She mustn't be lulled into a false sense of security by his mood; beneath the surface she had no doubt he was as furious as ever.

They were driving through the residential part of London, and Lauri felt her apprehension grow as Alex turned the car into an underground car park, parking the Ferrari next to the Rolls bearing his number plate.

She turned to look at him, knowing they were at his home. "What are we doing here?"

Alex gave her a scathing glance. "Use your common sense, Lauren. I can hardly go anywhere in a shirt covered in blood."

Her face flamed with color. "Oh. I—I forgot."

He grimaced. "I haven't, I can assure you of that."

She hung her head. "I'm really sorry I scratched you."

"You can't be any more sorry than I am." He swung out of the car to come round and open her door for her. "Come on."

"I—I'd rather wait here for you," she refused nervously. "And the reason I scratched you was because you were hurting me."

"I meant to hurt you," he told her grimly, not giving her a chance to make any more refusals, but pulling her unceremoniously out of the car and locking the door firmly behind her. "And I'll hurt you again if you don't stop acting like a hysterical idiot. I could be some time getting out of this shirt, and I have no intention of leaving you down here while I do it." He quirked an eyebrow. "You may decide to run away."

Lauri trailed along behind him as they walked the short distance to the lift, standing apart from him as it swished up the building. "What would be the point of running away?" she said hollowly.

"True," he drawled. "I'd just come after you." He waited for her to precede him out of the lift, moving to one of the only two doors on this floor, throwing open the door with a flourish. "In you go." He didn't wait for her to comply but pushed her inside.

The apartment was very much as she had imagined it to be—very modern, very luxurious, but lacking warmth, as was its occupier. Everywhere she looked was the stamp of wealth and good taste, and yet it lacked atmosphere, lacked that fundamental feeling that told you it was a home. It looked like one of the show houses she often admired in magazines but knew she could never live in.

Alex watched the play of emotions across her face, a mocking twist to his lips. "You don't like it," he stated.

"I—it—no," she answered truthfully. "No, I don't like it at all," she confirmed.

"I knew you wouldn't," he said with a shrug, throwing his car keys on the side table. "Make yourself at home," he added tauntingly. "I shouldn't be long." He disappeared through one of the many doors leading off this, the main room, into a room she presumed was his bedroom.

She couldn't make herself at home and he knew it—knew this wasn't the sort of place she could ever feel comfortable in. Consequently she was still standing awkwardly in the middle of the room when he came back out of the bedroom several minutes later. Her eyes widened as she took in his naked torso, the skin tanned a deep brown, four livid red scratch marks running down his chest. Lauri felt sick. Had she really inflicted those nasty-looking wounds?

Alex came to stand in front of her. "Here." He handed her a tube of antiseptic. "I'm sure you'll do a better job of it than I would."

"Yes, but I—" How could she tell him she daren't touch him, daren't because she was afraid of her reaction to him. She thrust the antiseptic back at him. "I'd rather not."

"Scared?" he taunted softly.

"Certainly not." She grabbed the tube out of his hand. "I was just afraid of hurting you. This could sting."

"I doubt it could hurt more than when you did it. Go on, Lauren, I'll be a brave boy," he mocked.

He wasn't a boy at all, that was the trouble! His chest and arms were firmly muscled, all the more noticeable as he stood with his hands on his waist. A fine sheen of dark hair covered his chest, curled slightly against his tanned skin. Lauri's hand shook as she applied the cream, her head bent as she concentrated determinedly on the task.

His skin felt smooth to the touch, the four jagged scratches marring the male beauty of him. She bit her lip, her concentration almost nil, her breathing ragged. She had to move away from him, had to escape the magnetism of the sensual aura he was emitting.

"Finished," she said huskily, her head still bent.

"No, I don't think you have," he contradicted softly.

Her eyes flew open. "But I have; you can see I have."

"No." He shook his head, taking the antiseptic out of her hand and throwing it on the table next to his car keys. "There's one place you missed with your healing touch."

Lauren frowned. "But I'm sure I—"

"It's right here, Lauren." He pulled her against him. "Right here," he repeated throatily, his mouth claiming and parting hers.

"My gown!" She wrenched away from him, looking down at the way the cream had stained the soft white material. "Look what you've done!" she gasped.

Alex pulled her back against him, his mouth caressing

her throat and bare shoulders. "It doesn't matter—you'll be taking it off in a minute."

"I—" Lauri pushed even harder against his restraining arms. "I most certainly will not!"

"You will." As if to prove his point she felt the zip of her gown being pulled down to the base of her spine, his hands moving freely across her bare back. "Like now." He gently bit her earlobe, not hard enough to cause pain but enough to make her aware that he was in control of the situation... and her. "We're going to prove that I can merit ten out of ten," he rasped, "on any woman's scale!"

"Alex, no.... Don't, *please*!"

He grinned down at her. "I think I'd like you to beg, Lauren. But not to be set free," he murmured against her lips. "I'd like you to beg for something quite different." He slipped the thin ribbon strap off one shoulder, the gown slipping down to reveal her bare breasts. "No bra," he said gruffly, making no effort to hide his reaction to her nakedness. "I like that."

"No...please. Please, Alex." She dragged the gown back up, her hands at her back as she tried to pull up the zip. "Let me go," she pleaded, her relief immense as she felt the zip slide easily up her spine.

His hands were at her nape. "You know you don't mean that." His mouth ate into hers, the kiss slow and languorous. "Come into the bedroom," he invited huskily.

"No! No, no, *no*!" She wrenched fully away from him. "You had no intention of taking me out this evening, did you?" she accused. "You intended bringing me back here all the time." Her eyes were deeply green in her anger.

"Eventually," he drawled. "But I did intend taking you out first."

"First," she echoed, startled.

"I always believe in wining and dining my girl friends before taking them to bed," he told her calmly.

"You—I—you aren't getting me into bed," she spluttered. "Whether you wine and dine me first or not." She swung away from him, for some reason her eyes alighting on the car keys he had discarded on entering the apartment. She snatched them up, almost running to the door.

"Where do you think you're going with my car keys?"

When she turned he was still standing in the place she had left him, making no effort to stop her or retrieve his keys. "Where do you think?" she scorned, throwing open the door.

"I hope you don't intend driving it," he drawled. "That, added to the accident you had at the beginning of the week, should be quite interesting to the police."

She met his gaze defiantly. "I have no intention of driving your car. But I do intend throwing these keys in the river. I only wish I could do the same to you!" She slammed the door as she left.

CHAPTER SEVEN

SHE WENT INTO A PUBLIC PHONE BOX and called for a taxi, getting him to stop on the way home so that she might do as she threatened and hurl the keys to the Ferrari into the murky depths of the river flowing below her.

She would teach Alexander Blair for thinking she would meekly jump into bed with him. It might be a childish gesture to dispose of his car keys, but it had given her infinite satisfaction, almost as good as being able to dispose of their owner in the same way. How dare he touch her so intimately, caress parts of her body no other man had ever seen.

Her cheeks were flushed as she ripped off the stained gown and threw it down on a chair, pulling on her ankle-length toweling robe. She would never be able to face him again, would have to leave her job, would have to— What was that noise? She frowned as she heard the opening and closing of the front door. Steve was home early, possibly because he realized she would be here on her own with Jane away.

She went downstairs, brushing her hair into a red gold cloud about her shoulders. "I'm home, Steve. I— My God, what are you doing here?" she exclaimed as she came up against Alexander Blair's hard chest.

"Lauren." He steadied her, wincing slightly. "Much as I would like you close to me, my chest is hurting like hell." He put her away from him.

"How did you get here?" she asked dazedly.

"By car, how else? I have a spare set of keys to the Ferrari, although I could have used the Rolls, you know."

"Oh, yes," she sighed. "I forgot about that. I—I'm sorry about your keys. It was a stupid thing to do."

"Yes," he agreed unhesitantly. "Very stupid."

"You goaded me into it," she said resentfully. "Talking about taking me to your bed in that way."

"Did you actually throw them in the river?"

She gave him a nervous glance. "Yes." She bit her lip.

"Really?"

"Mmm." She nodded.

To her surprise he smiled, the smile turning to a throaty chuckle and then finally to full laughter.

"Alex?" She was mesmerized by how attractive he looked when he laughed in this way without a trace of mockery.

He sobered, but the smile still remained. "Mmm?"

"You—you don't mind about your keys?"

"Well, of course I mind," he chuckled. "But it's what I should have known. You never do what's expected of you."

"Expected of me?" she flashed angrily. "If you mean going to bed with you, then no, I don't."

"I didn't mean that, as it happens. I meant that I didn't expect you to run off like that, and especially with my car keys."

"Is that why you threatened me with the police?" she challenged.

"That was done through sheer fright. I was terrified you were going to actually attempt to drive the Ferrari. I might let you do just that one day," he mused. "But only with me, never alone."

Lauri gave him a searching look. "I thought you never let anyone else drive you?"

He shrugged. "Perhaps I'll make you the exception."

She was aware that this was in the nature of an olive branch, but she wasn't going to be charmed so easily. She resented being treated like a little girl offered a treat to soothe her ruffled dignity. "I don't want to drive your car," she said primly. "And how dare you just walk into my home like this?"

"If I'd asked to come in you wouldn't have let me."

"No."

"Now you have your answer as to why I just walked in. I needed to see you, Lauren," he added huskily.

She gave him a suspicious look. After all, she was no more protected from him here than she had been at his apartment. Less so really, dressed as she was. She clutched her robe to her. "It could have waited until tomorrow."

"No." He shook his head. "I needed to see you tonight, to apologize for my behavior earlier." He put a rueful hand on his chest. "But you did anger me," he grimaced.

"You hurt me first," she defended.

A teasing light entered the blueness of his eyes. "I would readily kiss every bruise I inflicted," he offered.

"I bet you would." The beginning of a smile began to tug at the corners of her mouth. "But you aren't going to, not unless you would like a scratch down the other side, too."

"No, thanks. I may have deserved these, but you had challenged by prowess as your lover."

Lauri flushed fiery red. "You aren't my lover!"

"Yet."

"Never," she denied heatedly. "I'm not interested in having a lover. I just want to get on with enjoying my life."

"Oh, I'd make sure you did that." His voice was husky.

"I didn't mean in that way," she snapped. "Look,

you've apologized for your behavior, I've apologized for mine, so why don't we just call that the end of it?"

"The end of it?" His eyes were narrowed.

"We don't get on, Alex. We may be attracted to each other, but other than that we just argue. I don't want to see you anymore." By the look on his face, half anger, half disbelief, it would appear that not too many women had been the one to end a relationship with him. "I'm sorry." She shrugged.

"You're also a liar," he murmured, his eyes never leaving her face. "Come here."

She knew that look in his eyes of old. "N-no."

"Come here," he ordered, his face implacable.

"Please, Alex—"

"Come here!"

She went, standing just in front of him. "It's no good, Alex. We—" Her words were cut off by the descent of his mouth on hers, his lips moving over hers in a gentle, soul-destroying kiss. It was like none of the other kisses he had given her—her response was instantaneous and unreserved as he plundered her mouth again and again.

"Far from being no good," he murmured throatily against her lips. "That was *very* good. Too good to throw away because of a little misunderstanding."

Lauri jerked back, but remained in the circle of his arms when he refused to let her go. "*Little* misunderstanding?" she scorned. "I don't think it was little at all."

"Maybe not," he conceded. "You'll have to put it down to the difficult week I've had—meeting you for the first time being part of it," he added ruefully.

"Thanks!"

"Well, you have to admit that all of our encounters so far have been pretty traumatic. And then there was that meeting with Laurence." His face was grim. "Have you seen anything of him, by the way?"

"Me?" Lauri frowned. "Why on earth should I have seen him?"

Alex shrugged. "He seemed rather...taken with tyou."

She shook her head. "I don't think so. Maybe it just seemed that way because he realized he knew my mother. After all, he must have lost touch with most of his friends when he moved to Switzerland with your sister."

"Yes." Alex released her, his face harsh.

"Well, it can't have been very easy for him to come back after all this time and try to pick up the pieces," she defended.

"Easier than you think," he muttered, looking at her coldly. "So you liked him?"

"I don't like or dislike him; I don't know him. But I think if I got to know him I might like him very much."

"Oh, don't worry, you'll get to know him," Alex sneered. "Laurence was never one to pass up the chance of seeing a beautiful girl."

"I'm not beautiful...and as you just said, I'm only a girl. Goodness, he's old enough to be my father!"

"So he is," Alex nodded distantly. "What was your father like?"

"Oh, very nice," she gave a sad smile. "Very kind. He always had time to sit and talk to me, always listened to my problems, even though he had the responsibility of Jane and Steve, too."

"Your family seems to have suffered a lot of tragedies," he said dryly.

Her eyes flashed. "Death is not something one wants, it just happened that way. I loved my father very much."

"I can see that," he acknowledged gently.

"He and my mother were very happy together, proving that young marriages can be a success. Mummy was only eighteen when they married, and daddy was twenty. But they loved each other so much that they said it seemed silly to wait."

"They waited long enough to have you."

She nodded. "I think I was an afterthought. Some marriages are like that, aren't they, already complete even without a child. Mummy must have been in her mid thirties when I came along."

"Were they happy together even then?"

She gave him a puzzled look. "Of course they were. What a strange thing to ask."

"It wouldn't be the first time a wife has found herself another man," he rasped.

"How dare you! Really, Alex, you've gone too far this time," she snapped. "Sniping at me and being sarcastic are things I can take, but when you start maligning my mother's morals, the morals of a woman you know absolutely nothing about, then I think the time has come for you to go."

He looked at her coldly. "You're asking me to leave?"

"Yes," she confirmed rigidly.

"Because of a little harmless surmising on my part?"

"I don't consider it harmless. You were being very rude about my mother."

"I wasn't being rude, Lauren."

"Call me Lauri like everyone else does," she ordered shrilly. "I don't like being called Lauren." She didn't like this man calling her it, as if their relationship meant something special to him.

"I'll call you what I damn well please." His arrogance of their first meeting was back in evidence. "Lauri makes you sound like a little girl."

"And you like a woman in your arms," she sneered.

"Exactly," he drawled lazily. "And you become a woman in my arms, Lauren."

She glared at him, her eyes deeply green. "I hate you!" she told him vehemently. "You think a natural physical response to experienced lovemaking is enough to make me fall into your arms whenever you choose to snap your fingers. Well, it isn't! I could find any number of men who would evoke the same response."

"Little liar," he called her for the second time that evening.

She gasped indignantly. "You conceited, arrogant—"

"How you do love to call me names," he smiled, pulling her effortlessly against him. "And how I love to silence you." Which he did very effectively by kissing her!

"I wish you would stop doing that," she murmured some minutes later against his chest. "I—" She broke off as he seemed to flinch. "What is it? What's wrong?" She lifted her head to look at him.

"Nothing," he smiled down at her. "I think my shirt got stuck to the scratches. You pulled my shirt away by nestling against me like that. Not that I'm complaining," he grinned. "Far from it."

"Nevertheless—" she moved out of his arms "—you had better undo your shirt and let me have a look at your chest."

"Gladly." He shed his jacket with a grin, unbuttoning the black shirt he had changed into.

"That will be enough." Lauri stopped him from actually removing the shirt altogether, all too aware of the potency of this man. "Mmm." She bent her head to look at the angry red marks. "I think you ought to get a doctor to take a look at these."

"Oh, yes?" he taunted. "And what would I tell him?"

Color flooded her cheeks as she bit her bottom lip. "I never thought of that. But it doesn't look very good."

"That's just the antiseptic working. Don't you know the saying, 'it always gets worse before it gets better'?"

"Yes. But—"

"Don't fuss, Lauren." He made no effort to rebutton his shirt. "Now, would you like me to soothe your bruises better?"

"You're very persistent," she said lightly. "I think my bruises will disappear without any help from you."

"Sure?" His deep blue eyes held her mesmerized as his hands moved to the lapels of her toweling robe, slowly parting them to reveal her bare breasts and bikini briefs. He bent his head to kiss the hollows of her throat, moving lower and lower to her breasts, evoking pleasure with his tongue.

Lauri felt as if her body was melting into his, waves of ecstasy washing over her. This pleasure was like nothing else she had ever experienced, tension of a kind she didn't understand starting to build up inside her.

"Sure?" he repeated huskily, for the moment giving her respite from his lips but caressing her hips with his sensitive hands.

"No, I'm not sure." Her fingers were tangled in the dark thickness of his hair. "Kiss me some more, Alex," she pleaded.

"Do you love me, Lauren?" His lips were back on her breasts, a fire spreading through her whole body.

"I don't know," she moaned dazedly. "I— Oh, God!" She shuddered with emotion, her body feeling aflame with wanting.

"Do you?" he persisted, molding his thighs to hers to move against her in a sensuous rhythm.

"I—" Another sound besides their heated murmurings

was penetrating her dazed senses. It was the sound of some-one whistling! And it was coming from the kitchen. She broke away from Alex's embrace, her breathing labored as she fought for control. "There's someone else here." She clutched the robe to her, tying the belt with shaking fingers.

Alex made no move to button his shirt. "You didn't answer my question," he said huskily.

Lauri looked away. "No, I—I didn't. And I'm not going to. Please." She looked nervously toward the door that led to the kitchen. "Do up your shirt."

"Not until you answer me."

"You have no right to ask such a question." She moved toward him and began buttoning his shirt herself. "It has to be Steve out there," she snapped her agitation, "and you don't seem to care." She glared at him.

He shrugged. "I don't. I'm just interested in your answer."

"Help me do this," she pleaded, "before Steve comes in. If he sees you like this he'll—he'll think—"

His arms went about her. "Let him think," he mur-mured against her throat. "I couldn't give a damn."

"Well, I could!" She jerked away just as the door opened and her uncle came into the room.

Steve came to an abrupt halt as soon as he saw them. And Lauri wasn't surprised at the shocked expression on his face as he took in Alex's unbuttoned shirt and ruffled hair, and her only clothing a towelling robe.

"What's going on here?" he demanded.

Alex's mouth twisted with wry humor. "Don't be a fool, Prescott, it's obvious what's been 'going on.'"

"Lauri?" Steve's razor sharp gaze came to rest on her.

"Don't listen to him," she denied heatedly. "Alex was—we were—I—"

"Don't say any more," her uncle ordered. "I don't want a move by move account of it." He looked contemptuously at Alex. "Just what game do you think you're playing with my niece? I wouldn't have thought she was experienced enough for you," he added insultingly.

Alex buttoned his shirt with slow provocation. "She learns fast," he drawled.

"Why, you—"

Lauri's hand on Steve's arm stopped him from actually resorting to physical violence. "Leave it," she told him dully, her face suddenly very pale.

She could offer him no explanation for the way this situation looked without actually revealing what she had done to Alex's chest. Maybe letting him think what he did was better than him knowing the truth. As for Alex, she realized he had probably been annoyed by Steve's aggressive behavior but he didn't have to make the situation worse than it was. She learned fast, indeed!

"Leave it?" Steve repeated furiously. "It's one thing to take a girl to bed." He colored at his own words. "But quite another to go around boasting about it."

Lauri gasped. "Steve!"

"I wasn't boasting," Alex told the other man calmly, tucking his shirt back into the low waistband of his trousers. "And your niece and I have not been to bed together." He shrugged back into his jacket, straightening his cuff. "But then neither have we spent an innocent evening together."

Steve looked at them scathingly. "I can see that."

"You don't see anything of the kind. Now," Alex's voice lowered menacingly, "I'm only going to say this once, and then I don't want to speak of it again. Lauren and I are both old enough to make those sorts of decisions for ourselves. I want to sleep with her, yes, but when it happens—"

"*If* it happens," Steve corrected him fiercely.

"When it happens," Alex repeated, "it will be on her terms. And I think we both know that Lauren's terms will include a wedding ring."

"A...a wedding ring?" Steve echoed dazedly.

"That's right. Now I'll wish you both good-night." He bent to kiss Lauri gently on the lips. "I'll see you tomorrow, darling. Good night," he added harshly to Steve. "I'll see myself out."

"Lauri?" Steve queried uncertainly when the other man had left. "What did he mean?"

She was still trying to recover from the shock herself. Why on earth had Alex made that ridiculous statement? He knew she didn't want to get married, knew because she had told him herself. That was it! He had said it because he *did* know she didn't want to get married—or at least he thought she didn't. He had said that because it was a way of saving face and yet still remaining single. It would serve him right if she kept him to it. Of all the—

"Lauri!" Steve said impatiently. "What did he *mean*?"

"He didn't mean anything," she sighed. "He wouldn't have said it if you hadn't jumped to conclusions."

"Jumped to conclusions!" he said disgustedly. "I walk in here and find you both in a state of undress and I get accused of jumping to conclusions. My God, Lauri, you're naive! How long have you been seeing him?"

She bit her lip. "I haven't exactly been seeing him. I—we've had lunch together a couple of times."

"And after two lunches he almost has you in bed with him! Oh, yes, I'll accept that it hasn't gone that far yet," he said at her surprised expression. "But, good God, Lauri—Alexander Blair!"

"I know."

"Jane will be furious when she finds out."

Lauri looked away. "She already knows."

"She does?" he frowned. "But she didn't mention—"

"She found out tonight, too," she told him with a sigh.

"I bet she was as mad as I was."

"Shocked would be a better description," she admitted dryly.

"I'm not surprised." He began pacing the room. "The man's too damned old for you, for one thing. He's out of your league, Lauri."

"I seem to be managing all right so far." But getting more and more out of her depth every minute!

"So I noticed," Steve derided. "And what's all this talk about a wedding ring? You aren't marrying him!"

Her head went back in challenge. "I'll marry who I damned well please! And for your information, I haven't been asked."

"And if you are?" His eyes narrowed.

"I'll refuse." Although she knew there was no possibility of Alex proposing. This way he had made it seem as if it was her decision not to marry him. As if someone like him would even propose to a nonentity like her.

"You . . . you would refuse?"

"Of course I would," she scorned. "You've already said it, Steve; the man's out of my league."

"My niece is good enough to marry anyone!"

She had to laugh at his about-face. "You are funny," she said on his inquiring look. "You can't make up your mind whether to be outraged at the situation you think you interrupted, or indignant because I don't consider myself a suitable candidate for the role of Mrs. Alexander Blair."

"So you *were* the Lauren with the sexy voice," he mused. "That must have infuriated Jane."

"Yes," she acknowledged with a sigh. "You could say that."

"Did she go to Robin's parents'?"

"After a bit of persuading. She wasn't too happy about leaving me alone with Alex," she explained.

"I don't suppose she was. One of these days you can tell me exactly what I *did* interrupt."

She blushed. "I already told you, it was nothing. I think you should know Jane's seriously contemplating marrying Robin."

"God, no!"

"Mmm," she nodded.

"But he's all wrong for her."

"I know. But she muttered something about him being steady and reliable and never letting her down."

"He'll never let her down because he *is* steady and reliable. The man's only half alive!"

"I know that, too." She shrugged. "I just thought I should warn you."

"Thanks," he grimaced. "When she gets back I'll try to talk some sense into her."

"I think you'll be too late."

"Too late?"

"I think Robin intends proposing this weekend. As long as she meets mummy and daddy's approval, of course."

He looked ready to explode. "Damned cheek! She's too damned good for him, if anything. And what sort of man is he that he has to have his parents' approval at his age?"

"Alex said the same— Well, he did," she insisted. "He said that if Jane were interested enough in him to marry him, he wouldn't care what his parents thought."

"My God, he isn't after Jane, too?"

Lauri laughed at his expression. "I don't think so. He just likes her."

"I doubt the feeling is reciprocated now that she knows he's been taking you out. Okay, okay, enough said," he muttered as she stiffened angrily. "But I don't like it."

"I'll note your disapproval," she teased. "Now I for one am off to bed. I'd advise you to do the same." She got to the bottom of the stairs before turning to face him, a mischievous look in her eyes. "I bet you sobered up a lot quicker than you got drunk," she taunted.

"I wasn't drunk," he retorted indignantly. "Just slightly merry. But I'm certainly sober now."

She was still laughing when she entered her bedroom, although her humor died as soon as she had closed the door behind her. Damn Alex Blair and his mischief making. Whatever devil had entered his system, she would let him know she didn't appreciate it. He had been so completely different tonight, almost seeming to despise her at times—when he wasn't making love to her, that is.

If only he weren't so potent to her senses. But it was no use denying the desire he made her feel—he knew of it every time he touched her. She dreaded to think what would have happened if Steve hadn't come home when he did; she could even now be in Alex's arms. He would be a lover who took his time, gave her every pleasure she had ever dreamed of before taking his own passion to its body-shattering conclusion.

Her body still tingled where he had touched her, although far from soothing her bruises she thought he may have inflicted a few more. And why had he been trying to make her confess her love for him, playing with her body in a way that would ultimately have made her tell him anything he wanted to hear? The fact that she did love him, and she knew she could no longer deny that to herself at least, would have to remain her secret. There would be no denying him if he knew of her true feelings.

STEVE WAS ON HIS THIRD CUP OF COFFEE by the time she came down the next morning. "God, I had a lousy night," he groaned.

"You probably had more to drink than you realized," she said unsympathetically.

He scowled at her. "It wasn't the drink. It was worry about you that kept me awake."

"Me?" She raised her eyebrows, setting about cooking their bacon and eggs for breakfast. "One egg or two?" she asked absently.

"Two. And don't change the subject."

She smiled. "Whatever's wrong with you, it hasn't affected your appetite."

"Lauri!"

"All right," she sighed. "Why were you worried about me?"

"You know why! It can't go on, Lauri. God, what will everyone at work say if they find out about you and Blair?"

"Sorry." Her cheerful voice belied that statement. "They already know. It's been buzzing around the building all week."

"Oh, *God*," he groaned.

"Stop being so melodramatic, Steve. I must say I dreaded the gossip, too, but it will soon die down." As soon as she had told Alex she couldn't see him anymore! She would have to leave Blair's, there was no other answer for it. She might think she was in love with Alex now, but if she continued to see him it could only become worse. She would become dependent upon him, was even now becoming so, and when he lost interest, which could happen at any time, she would simply fall apart.

"You obviously don't know office gossip," Steve grimaced. "It can be murder."

Having already sampled some of it, she was well aware of it. People stared at her wherever she went at work, conversations stopped when she walked into a room, and worst of all, hardly anyone spoke to her. Oh, she knew all about office gossip, but she hadn't let that frighten her into not seeing Alex; that decision was being made completely removed from anything but the way she had discovered she felt about him, her love completely different to the emotion he felt for her.

"It's just a nine days' wonder," she dismissed. "And certainly not enough to influence your getting to the top of the salesman's list," she added teasingly.

"As if I— Stop teasing, Lauri," he said angrily, as she laughed outright at his indignation. "This is a serious matter."

She put his breakfast down in front of him. "Only if you let it be. And I'm certainly not going to do that." She sat down opposite him to eat her own meal.

Steve shook his head wonderingly. "You're so calm about this. Don't you realize whom you're dating!"

Oh, she realized, and she found it no less daunting, did he but know it. "I'm not dating him," she said calmly. "I've gone out with him a couple of times, that's all."

He attacked the food on his plate as if he would like it to be Alexander Blair. "I suppose it's all my fault," he groaned. "If I hadn't let you drive my car you wouldn't have crashed into him and probably never have spoken to him."

"That's ridiculous, Steve, and you know it. As it happens, I met him again quite by chance. I was in the lift when he got in it."

"Oh." Steve still didn't look very happy. "But even so, he may not have spoken to you if it hadn't been for the accident."

Remembering what she had been doing when the lift doors opened, kissing Daryl, she thought it very likely that Alex would have spoken to her anyway. And it hadn't stopped at talking that time, either! "I think he may have done," she said huskily.

"Maybe. When's lover boy going to get here today?"

Lauri smiled. "I don't think either term applies to Alex. And I have no idea what time he'll be here." But she had plenty to talk to him about when he did get here!

"He just turns up when he— My God!" he broke off as the doorbell rang. "Doesn't he even believe in letting a man finish his breakfast before he calls?" He pushed his empty plate away moodily.

"But you have finished. And it is almost eleven o'clock."

"On a Sunday," he said disgustedly. "Everyone has a lay-in on a Sunday."

"Obviously not Alex."

"Obviously. Well, go and let him in before he kicks the door down. I'm going back to bed."

"But—"

"I'm sure you don't need me around."

Lauri sighed as he stomped up the stairs. She shrugged, moving to open the door. "Alex, I—" Her words faded in her throat as she saw that it wasn't Alex at all, but Laurence Daniels. And he looked terrible, completely haggard.

CHAPTER EIGHT

"HELLO," SHE GREETED SHYLY.

"Lauri," he returned huskily.

She couldn't get over how ill he looked, his tan having faded almost completely, a permanent whiteness about his taut mouth. "Would you like to come in?" she invited gently.

The eyes behind the smoky lenses seemed to brighten. "You wouldn't mind?"

Lauri smiled, opening the door wider. "Of course not. Come through to the lounge." She saw him seated, noticing that he seemed thinner than ever. "Would you like a cup of coffee or something?"

"Coffee would be nice," he accepted, sitting tensely on the edge of the armchair.

"I— Have you eaten?"

"Eaten?" he blinked his puzzlement. "Breakfast, you mean?"

She nodded. "Or breakfast yesterday, or lunch, or dinner?"

"I—um—" He put a hand up to his graying temple. "I think I had lunch."

"But no dinner, and no breakfast this morning?"

He shook his head. "I don't believe so, no."

"Right. Well, you're going to have breakfast now." She hesitated in the doorway. "Would you like to come into the kitchen and talk to me while I cook, or would you rather just sit there quietly?''

Laurence stood up. "I've had enough silence the last few days to last me a lifetime. Besides, it's too long since I saw a woman moving about the kitchen preparing me a meal. '' He smiled ruefully.

Lauri pulled out a bar stool for him to sit down on. "Bacon and eggs?''

"Lovely.'' He seemed to be shedding some of his tension. "This is very kind of you, considering I'm a stranger to you.''

"I don't consider you a stranger.'' And strangely enough she didn't. Maybe it was the fact that he had known her parents that made him seem like a friend—whatever it was, she felt completely at ease with him.

"I'm glad,'' he smiled at her. "Would you like me to do anything—make the coffee, lay the table?''

"No, you just sit there.''

It didn't take long to prepare his meal and give him coffee, and she watched with satisfaction as he looked in anticipation at his bacon and eggs.

He hesitated. "Aren't you having any?''

"I've already eaten. But you go ahead; I'll join you in a coffee. That is, if you don't mind having an audience while you eat?''

"I don't mind at all. It's nice just to have company.''

Lauri frowned. "You haven't seen Alex?''

"Not since the two of you picked me up at the airport. You may have noticed that he and I don't exactly get on together.''

"Well...neither of you tried to hide it.''

"No,'' he acknowledged slowly. "I'm afraid I shattered Alex's illusions about me at an age when he was very impressionable. Did he tell you about it?''

Lauri bit her lip, not wanting to lie, and yet not wanting to hurt this strangely vulnerable man. "He mentioned some disagreement you had years ago," she prevaricated.

Laurence laughed. "It wasn't a disagreement, and I'm sure Alex more than mentioned it. I committed a great sin as far as he was concerned, and he's never forgiven me for it. On reflection I think it would have been better if I had broken away from Beth completely, instead of trying to live year after year as if our marriage was perfectly normal."

"More coffee?" Lauri asked awkwardly.

"Thank you." He held out his cup while she refilled it. "Have I embarrassed you, talking to you so frankly?"

"No, of course not." She wanted desperately to erase that frown of anxiety from his brow. "Maybe being a stranger I'm the ideal person to talk to."

He gave a rueful smile. "I don't consider you a stranger, either, Lauri."

"Sorry," she said huskily. "I didn't mean it quite like that."

"I know." His hand covered hers as it rested on the table. "You're very like your mother," he said huskily.

"I am?" She looked startled. "But I'm nothing like her, or any other member of my family, come to that."

"I didn't mean in looks—that red gold hair and green eyes is certainly unusual in your family, that's why I—" He drew a deep ragged breath. "Never mind that. I meant that you're kind and gentle like your mother was."

"I never knew her that well," Lauri told him regretfully. "But I remember her as being beautiful."

He nodded. "She was, very. Without her I don't think I could have got through the first years after Beth's accident."

"You mean my mother helped you?"

"Yes, she helped me." He seemed to have withdrawn

into his thoughts. "Sorry." He shook his head as if to clear his mind. "Bad memories," he shuddered.

"Alex told me you lost your son in the accident," she said gently. "That must have been awful for you."

"Yes, awful. Jamie was only five."

"Terrible to lose your child."

"Terrible," he echoed, that strange look back in his eyes. "Even worse to lose the woman you love."

"Alex said it happened six months ago."

"What?" He looked startled.

"Alex said your wife died six months ago," she explained.

"Oh," he nodded. "Yes, that's right."

"Hardly time for the pain of her death to have lessened," she sympathized.

"I was very fond of my wife, Lauri, but— What was that?" he asked sharply as a door slammed upstairs. His eyes narrowed. "Is Alex here?"

She blushed at the implication behind that question. "No, of course he isn't. He doesn't stay here. We don't sleep together."

"I'm sorry, my dear." Laurence was instantly contrite. "It's just that knowing my brother-in-law as I do—well, he has a certain reputation."

"I know. But the person upstairs is Steve, my uncle."

"Ah, yes, I know him. He must be in his mid-twenties by now?"

"Yes. But I—I didn't know the two of you knew each other."

"We don't," Laurence smiled. "I met him once or twice, that's all. I doubt he would remember me; he could only have been about seven or eight at the time."

"I suppose so."

"Have you lived in this house long?" he asked interestedly. "I remember that the family lived on the other side of town when I knew them."

Lauri frowned. "I can never remember living anywhere else, so I suppose we must have been here some time."

"Then it's lucky I met you with Alex. I would never have been able to find you otherwise. And that would have been a great shame in the circumstances."

"Because you knew my mother," she nodded.

"Of course. By knowing you I feel close to her."

Lauri frowned. "Mr. Daniels—"

"Laurence, please."

"Very well...Laurence. Did you—oh, damn." She bit her lip as the doorbell rang for the second time that morning. It could only be one person, Alex. "I—I'll just see who it is."

He stood up. "Would you like me to leave?"

"Don't be silly." She gave a light laugh. "Come through to the lounge. Bring your coffee with you. I shouldn't be long."

She was right about the identity of her visitor. Alex stood on the doorstep, more casually dressed than she had ever seen him: the faded denims fitting low down on his hips, the black silk shirt casually unbuttoned down his chest. He took Lauri's breath away, although she made an effort to hide her suddenly racing pulse and ragged breathing.

"Alex." She gave a strained smile.

He bent to kiss her lightly on the lips. "Right first time," he taunted. "Can I come in or am I to be made to stand on the doorstep all day?"

"You're a bit early. I've barely finished eating my breakfast."

Blue eyes narrowed. "Do I come in or don't I?"

"I—"

"I think Lauri is a little reluctant to ask you in because I'm here, Alex." Laurence Daniels was suddenly standing behind her.

Alex's features set harshly, his gaze icy cold. "What are you doing here?" he demanded angrily.

"Alex!" Lauri gasped. "This is my home. *You* are the visitor."

He looked down at her with narrowed eyes, his face rigid. "What does that mean?" he asked dangerously soft.

"It means—it means that *I* choose who enters my home."

"And you wanted Laurence here," he snapped. "My God," he addressed the other man. "You didn't waste much time. I knew you would be around here some time. You just couldn't stay away, could you?"

"I came to see Lauri."

"Oh, I know that," Alex sneered. "I also know why. The question is, does she?"

"No," Laurence's voice sounded strangulated, his face white.

"Are you going to tell her?"

"Alex—"

"Are you?" he demanded hardly.

"I—God, I don't know!" Laurence really looked ill now, as haggard as he had when he arrived here.

Laurie went to him, her arm going about his waist as he seemed to stagger.

"Leave him alone," she told Alex vehemently. "Can't you see he's ill?"

"People like him go on forever," Alex said with dislike.

She felt Laurence go limp against her, and she couldn't

prevent him from crumpling to the ground. "My God—" It was her turn to pale now. "Alex!"

He instantly moved forward, coming down on one knee beside his brother-in-law. He released Laurence's tie, feeling for a pulse. "He's still alive," he muttered.

"No thanks to you! Look how shallow his breathing is. You've killed him, you know, you with your sarcasm and nasty comments. You've killed him!" Her voice rose shrilly.

"Don't get hysterical, Lauren," Alex ordered harshly. "That's the last thing we need right now. Call an ambulance. We have to get him to hospital as quickly as possible."

"He's going to die, I know he's going to die! It's all your fault. You—" Her words came to an abrupt halt as Alex struck her hard across one cheek, tears of pain welling up and cascading down her cheek. "You swine!" she choked.

"For once I don't give a damn what you call me. Get an ambulance here, Lauren. Now!"

She picked up the telephone immediately, not sure afterward how she had managed to give the relative information to the woman on the other end of the line. But somehow she must have done because it seemed only seconds later that the ambulance arrived.

"Are you traveling with him?" one of the ambulance men asked her.

She looked anxiously at Alex. He was Laurence's nearest relative, no matter how much he wished he weren't. "Alex...?"

"You go with him, Lauren." He sounded strange, not at all his usual arrogant self. "I'll follow in the car. We're going to need transport back later."

"All right." She grabbed her jacket. "My God—Steve!

He's upstairs in bed. I—I can't just leave without telling him what's happened."

"I don't know who this Steve is, love," the ambulance man remarked. "But if you want your dad to get to the hospital alive we have to leave now."

"Oh, but he isn't—"

"Leave it, Lauren." Alex pulled her after the men carrying the stretcher. "Let's just get Laurence to the hospital," he said raggedly.

"You do care," she said dazedly. "Then why—"

"It's become a habit to hate him," he answered harshly. "Get going, Lauren." He bent to kiss her hard on the mouth. "I'll see you at the hospital."

Laurence seemed very still and gray to her; she felt sure he must already be dead. "Is he—is he—"

"He's holding on, love," the man traveling in the back of the ambulance with her assured her.

"Thank God." She swallowed hard.

"Don't worry, we'll soon have him there."

It felt very strange to be traveling at high speed in an ambulance furiously ringing its bell. Laurence looked so ill! She was relieved when they at last reached the hospital and she could once again let Alex take control.

"Oh, Alex." She collapsed against him as they waited to find out how Laurence was. "This is just awful."

"Yes. Did—did Laurence regain consciousness at all?"

She shook her head. "They were giving him oxygen most of the way."

"So he had no chance to speak to you?"

"No. Alex, why did he collapse like that?" she quavered. "I know the two of you were arguing, but it—it didn't seem any worse than the last time I saw you together."

"To Laurence it was," he said grimly.

"But he—" They both looked up as a nurse came toward them, but she walked straight past them. "I hate this waiting about," Lauri shuddered.

"I'll get us some coffee from the machine over there. Just sit down, Lauren, and stay calm."

She sipped gratefully at the hot liquid that tasted like a cross between coffee and tea, but was distinctive as neither. "How long will they be, do you think?"

"Still worried about Steve?" he sneered.

Angry spots of color appeared in her pale cheeks. "That's a foul thing to say," she snapped. "I just wondered how long it would be before we knew... either way."

Alex shrugged, hunched over his own coffee cup, lines of tension grooved into his face. "Not long, I should think. What was he doing at your place this morning?"

"Just visiting," she told him resentfully.

"Since when?"

"Since about half an hour before you arrived. I gave him breakfast, actually. He hasn't been taking care of himself, and I think he was lonely." The last was almost a rebuke.

"Lonely!" Alex gave a harsh laugh. "He should have thought of that before he—" He stopped abruptly.

"Before he what?" Lauri prompted.

"It isn't important. This is a hell of a time to be bringing up old grievances, even if they do affect the present." He looked about them impatiently. "Why the hell doesn't someone let us know how he is?" he snapped.

"They will, Alex." She put a hand soothingly on his arm. "You really are worried about him, aren't you?"

His face hardened. "I wouldn't want his death on my conscience," he told her abruptly.

"It isn't only that," Lauri rebuked gently. "You care for him, care what happens to him."

He sighed. "I suppose I do, although why the hell I should.... I just can't forget what he did to my sister."

"Maybe it wasn't all one-sided. You said that he and your sister weren't happy together even before the accident. They may even have parted if the accident hadn't happened. And you did say there was only the one affair— maybe he loved this other woman. If he did it must have been a very hard decision to choose to stay with a woman who didn't love him when the chance of happiness beckoned him."

Alex gave a strained smile. "You're seeing this through a romantic haze, Lauren. What makes you think this other woman was free to love him?"

"Well— Because—"

"She wasn't. She was a married woman. Laurence had an affair with her and walked out when it got too hot to handle, using his crippled wife as an excuse."

"How do you know all this?" she asked sharply.

"Most of it I know to be fact; the rest is obvious."

She shook her head. "Not to me. There could have been any number of reasons—"

"You like him, don't you?" Alex cut in.

She colored bright red. "Why shouldn't I?" She was on the defensive. "What he did in the past is none of my business. I like the man he is now."

"I hope you still feel that way later today."

"What do you mean?" Lauri asked sharply.

Alex shrugged. "It isn't up to me to tell you, although I'm sure Laurence thinks that I will. No doubt he'll tell you himself in his own time."

"This is hardly the time to keep secrets."

"It isn't my secret," he rasped. "Thank God!"

"Does this secret concern me?"

"Oh, yes," he gave a harsh laugh.

"Then I have a right to know," she told him stubbornly.

"Not this." He shook his head. "It may once have given me great pleasure to hurt Laurence, but not anymore."

Lauri frowned. "But if it concerns me—"

"Not now, Lauren." He stood up. "The doctor's coming over."

"Mr. Daniels's relatives?" The young doctor stood in front of them—a tired-looking man with long hair that grew wildly down to his shoulders.

"Yes," Alex nodded tersely.

"Well, I'm afraid Mr. Daniels has suffered a slight heart attack. You probably guessed that?"

"Yes." Again Alex nodded.

"Yes, well, I won't deny the seriousness of it, but for the moment he's out of danger. Rest and no worries should take care of his speedy recovery."

"Oh, thank God for that." Lauri felt quite faint, not realizing the strain she had been under until this moment. "Thank God!"

Alex turned to her. "Sit down, darling," he encouraged gently. "It's been a great shock for you."

Lauri did as he said, coloring at his easy use of the endearment. "When will we be able to see him?" she asked the doctor.

"He's in intensive care at the moment, but later on today he should be moved to a private ward. Your instructions, I believe, Mr. Blair?"

"That's right." Even in denims and casual shirt Alex managed to exude an aura of authority.

"You and your wife can go and see him for two minutes now. No more than that," the doctor warned. "Mr. Daniels is still a very sick man."

"We understand. And thank you."

"Why didn't you tell him I'm not your wife?" Lauri demanded as soon as the harassed-looking doctor had left them in order to go to another emergency.

Alex shrugged. "It wasn't important."

"It was to me! So far today I've been called Laurence's daughter and your wife, neither of which description is true."

"Let's go and see Laurence," he said impatiently. "What does it matter what or who people think you are," he snapped. "Stop being so damned stupid."

Her mouth was set in an angry line but she made no comment, realizing that to argue with him now would be in very poor taste. No matter how he denied it, he was concerned for his brother-in-law, conscious that it was the argument between them that had caused the other man's collapse.

Laurence was awake when they entered the room, although the grayness of his face and the blue tinge to his mouth showed how ill he still was. He put a hand out toward Lauri when he saw her, a slight smile on his lips as she took it into her own.

"Stupid thing to do," he muttered.

Lauri smiled. "It didn't happen through choice."

He turned to Alex. "Not your fault," he said weakly. "I've been heading for this for a long time."

"But I didn't have to precipitate it," Alex scowled. "Lauren said it was my fault, and it was. I'm sorry, Laurence. I had no right to try to interfere."

"Then you haven't—"

"No, I haven't," Alex sighed. "We'll be back to see you tonight. You'll be better for a few hours' rest. And don't worry about a thing."

Lauri squeezed Laurence's hand. "I'll come back to-night, too, shall I?"

His eyes lighted up. "Please," he said huskily.

"She'll come with me," Alex told him.

"I—"

"Won't you?" His hand was under the hair at her nape, exerting pressure.

She squirmed as much as she could without letting Laurence know what was going on. "Yes," she finally agreed. "Rest now," she advised the man in the bed.

She turned on Alex as soon as they were in the Ferrari on their way to her home. "You're getting altogether too bossy for your own good," she snapped. "I don't like being ordered about."

"Did you want to cause a scene in front of Laurence?"

"You know I didn't. But I can find my own way to the hospital tonight. If Laurence hadn't been there this morn-ing I would have told you that I don't want to see you again."

"Because of last night?"

"Of course because of last night!"

"Because I tried to make you admit you love me?" he taunted.

"Because you tried to *make love* to me," she corrected.

"And I would have succeeded, too, if Steve hadn't inter-rupted."

Lauri blushed. "I know that," she admitted huskily. "That's why I don't want to be alone with you anymore."

He gave her a mocking glance. "You're alone with me now."

"It isn't the same thing," she said irritably.

"You still haven't told me whether or not you're in love with me."

"And I don't intend to!"

"How about if I tell you first?" he asked throatily.

Lauri's mouth set. "I'm not going to have an affair with you, so you can stop the lies."

He raised dark eyebrows. "Why should I lie?"

"Well, it certainly isn't the truth. I may like you . . . a lot," she added at his scornful snort. "But I'm certainly not going to fall for that old routine about loving me and how about I prove I love you by hopping into bed with you, of course."

"Did I ask for proof?"

She stared rigidly ahead, glad that they were almost at her home. "Not yet, but you would. And then when you got tired of me you would say it was all a mistake, that you didn't love me after all."

"And what makes you think I would get tired of you?" He had stopped the car outside the house and had turned in his seat to look at her, his hand caressing the nape he had bruised earlier at the hospital. "So far, knowing you has been far from dull," he drawled.

"My . . . inexperience would soon pall."

Alex grinned. "You wouldn't stay inexperienced for long."

"I'm sure you're only too willing to teach me everything you know," Lauri retorted sarcastically.

"Mmm—" His hand still caressed her. "And that should take some time."

"I'll bet." She jerked away from him. "Forget it, Alex."

"But you told me at the start that an affair would suit you better than marriage."

Her eyes flashed deeply green. "Maybe it would, if I loved someone and they loved me! But I'll make sure it's someone who's as innocent as I am."

"For innocent read inexperienced," Alex mocked.

"Perhaps," she snapped, pushing open the car door. "But I won't just be another conquest for any man!" She got out onto the pavement. "Goodbye, Alex."

He restarted the engine. "I'll see you later, Lauren. We'll be going to the hospital together. Seven o'clock. Be ready."

Steve was out when she let herself into the house and so she was able to fume in private. She had been right to presume Alex's mention of marriage to Steve was just a ruse; his suggestion of an affair was evidence of that. And he was a man who didn't give up easily, so she would have to beware now that she knew his intention.

Jane telephoned just before five to say she and Robin would be leaving shortly. And by her tone she would have a lot to say to Lauri when she got here. All the more reasons for Lauri to be out, and besides, she had told Laurence she would visit him.

Alex wasn't put off by her cool attitude toward him later that evening, talking to her easily about impersonal subjects as they drove to the hospital. Most of his conversation required no answer, and so she didn't have the satisfaction of showing him she wasn't speaking to him. Damn him!

"Cheer up, Lauren," he told her as they entered the hospital. "I'm sure you won't help Laurence with that long face."

"I had no intention of presenting a long face to him," she snapped, glaring at him.

"Only to me, hmm?" he taunted.

"Go to hell!" she flared, the scowl fading from her features as she entered Laurence's room. She was glad to see that he looked slightly better, a little more color to his face, the blue tinge to his skin almost gone. "How do you feel now?" she asked him gently.

"I feel rather stupid." He gave a rueful smile. "Ah,

Alex." His gaze passed to the man who had entered the room behind her. "I'm glad you're here."

"As it was my fault this happened, it would have been pretty callous not to have visited you," Alex said gruffly. "I should have known... Beth said something about a weak heart."

"I'm fine if I take care of myself."

"Which Lauren says you haven't been doing."

Laurence smiled at her. "With one thing and another it was all too much for me." He looked keenly at Alex. "I'm sure you know what I mean."

"Yes," Alex nodded.

"I wonder," Laurence said slowly, "if I might have a few minutes alone with Lauri?"

Alex frowned. "I don't think now would be a good time; her mood isn't very receptive at the moment."

"It has to come some time, Alex."

"But not now."

"Yes!" Laurence insisted with as much force as he could in his weakened condition. "I have to tell her. I want Lauri to know the truth."

"It's your decision, of course," Alex said coolly. "But I would advise against it for the moment."

"Against what, for heaven's sake?" Lauri was sick of this cross talk they indulged in in front of her. "What do you want to tell me?" she asked the older man.

"Alex—please," Laurence prompted.

"Okay," he sighed. "But don't say I didn't warn you. I'll be outside...if you need me."

Laurence waited for him to leave before seizing Lauri's hand. "I...I wanted to talk to you alone because there's something I have to tell you—*need* to tell you, for my sanity."

She looked puzzled by his earnest expression. "Surely it can't be that serious, whatever it is."

"I'm afraid it is very serious." He took his glasses off to rub his eyes, looking down at his hand as it pleated the sheet. "You see, Lauri, I— Oh, God, there's just no easy way to tell you this! I'm your father, Lauri, your real father!"

She recoiled as if he had hit her, wrenching her hand away from his. "No! You...you're lying!" She stared at him in horror.

"No, Lauri, I'm not." He raised his lids, looking at her with eyes as deeply green as her own.

CHAPTER NINE

LAURI HAD NEVER REALIZED that he had green eyes, the tinted lenses of his glasses making them appear a smoky brown. But the coincidence of their eye color didn't make him her father!

Laurence looked at her pleadingly. "I know this is a shock for you, Lauri, but I—"

"Shock!" she repeated almost hysterically. "It's a fairy tale, a fabrication of a sick man's mind."

"No, Lauri." He shook his head, reaching over for his wallet. It was just out of his grasp. "Pass it to me—please."

She pushed it within his reach, stepping back before he could make any further attempt to touch her. "Why are you telling these lies?" There were tears in her eyes. "Why are you trying to hurt me?"

"I don't want to hurt you, God knows," he groaned. "But you're my daughter, and—"

"I'm not!" she cried shrilly, putting her hands childishly over her ears. "I'm not, I'm not, I'm *not*!"

"Lauri? Lauri, come here," he encouraged gently. "I have something I want to show you."

She ignored his outstretched hand. "What is it?"

"A photograph."

She gave him a sharp look. "Of whom?"

"Come and see," he invited softly.

"No! I— What you're telling me is that my mother—that she was the one—that you and she—"

"Loved each other," he finished.

She gave a harsh laugh. "Is that the way you like to think of your sordid affair, the affair you had while your wife was at home, a helpless cripple in a wheelchair?"

"Your mother and I loved each other," his voice hardened angrily. "And there was nothing sordid about that love. Now come over here!" he ordered.

Her eyes widened indignantly at his command, but she went to his side anyway. He held out the photograph to her, an old faded photograph with a brown tinge to everything. The coloring of the middle-aged woman was impossible to guess, but the face—the face was Lauri's own! The widely spaced eyes, uptilted freckle-smattered nose and wide, smiling mouth—all her own features, and yet the age of the photograph denied it being her.

"Who...?"

"My mother, your grandmother."

"No!" She threw the photograph down onto the bed as if it had stung her. "I—I don't want to hear any more." She ran to the door. "I won't *listen* to any more."

"In my experience running away from a situation has never solved it," he told her in a strained voice. "And if you leave now you will be running away, postponing the inevitable."

"Then I'll postpone it!" she said shrilly. "You stay away from me, just stay away!"

"I can't do that, Lauri," he told her sadly. "I lost one child through death; I certainly don't intend losing another one—for any reason."

"I'm not your child," she told him vehemently. "Oh, I'm not denying you could be my father—*could* be," she repeated warningly. "That photograph is pretty damning—undeniable evidence, you could say. But the act of making a child doesn't make you my father."

"Lauri—"

"I'm sorry. I know you're ill, but I don't ever want to see or hear from you again. Not ever!" She slammed out of the room.

Alex stood up on her exit, coming toward her with long strides. "Lauren—"

"Don't touch me!" She evaded his grasp, a hundred pounds of fury as she glared her hatred at him. "You knew about this," she accused. "You've known about this from the start."

He put his hands savagely in his denim pockets. "Not from the start, Lauren; only since we picked Laurence up at the airport. I told you when we went to lunch on Tuesday that you reminded me of someone. As soon as I saw the two of you together I knew who that someone was."

So that was the reason for his sudden cruelty, for the veiled argument between Laurence and himself as they traveled back into town. "What a shock for you, Alex," she scorned. "To find I'm the daughter of the man you most despise. God, how ironic!" She began to laugh, a hysterical laugh that went on and on.

"Stop that!" One of his hands snaked out and slapped her hard across the face.

"Oh, I'll stop." She made no attempt to touch her throbbing cheek. "In fact, I'll remove myself completely. And I'll repeat to you what I told *him*. I don't ever want to see either of you again."

Her flight was one of haste, wanting only to get away, to think, to—God, it couldn't be true, Laurence Daniels couldn't be her *father*!

She walked and walked, not wanting to think and yet finding she could do little else. To think that her mother and Laurence Daniels had been lovers, that they had deceived her father, had even foisted their love child onto him. Her father had never known of the affair, of that Lauri felt certain; he could never have been so loving toward her if he had known.

To think that her mother had been the woman Laurence Daniels deceived his wife with, that Alex had been right about it being a married woman. By the time the affair had ended there had been a child, a child whom her father had accepted as being his own. Probably because it had never occurred to him that his beautiful wife could be unfaithful to him.

Did Jane and Steve suspect anything of her parenthood? After all, they had been seventeen and eight at the time, quite old enough to realize that their brother's wife had another man. Hadn't Laurence said he had seen Steve a couple of times, and he couldn't have done that unless Adelle had taken him along on some of their meetings.

She knew that what Laurence Daniels had told her was the truth ... and she hated him for it. But she hated Alex Blair, too! He had known since their meeting on Wednesday, and that was the reason he had made no attempt to see her after that; why he had called for her last night and deliberately caused trouble with her aunt and uncle. He had decided to pay her back, too, for the pain his sister had suffered.

She had meant it about not seeing either of them again. She despised Laurence Daniels for his affair with her mother, and she hated Alex for what he had tried to do to her last night. If she had admitted loving him, had let him make love to her, no doubt he would then have taken great pleasure in informing her she meant nothing to him, that he had done it only because of her relationship to Laurence. Little did he know that he still had his revenge: she was still insanely in love with him.

Jane and Robin were in the lounge when she finally arrived home, and much as she would have liked to have gone straight to her room, she knew her aunt would never let her escape that easily. If only Jane realized the shock she had received today.

Jane stood up on her entrance. "Lauri, I— Goodness are you ill?" She rushed to her side. "What's happened?"

"Nothing." Lauri sat down...before she fell down.

Jane's mouth set. "It was Alexander Blair," she said grimly. "He said you were upset, but he didn't say he was the cause of it."

She gave her aunt a sharp look. "You've heard from Alex?" That was something she hadn't expected.

"He came round."

"Alex did?" she frowned.

"Yes, darling," Jane confirmed gently. "He seemed... concerned."

"I'll bet he was," she acknowledged grimly.

"What happened?" Jane frowned. "Did he—"

"Oh, no." Lauri's smile was bitter. "Nothing like that. Alex Blair doesn't use force; he has other, more subtle ways of getting what he wants. He would never hurt a woman that way."

"But he has hurt you very much. I can tell that."

Lauri shook her head. "Not him. At least, only partly."

Robin stood up, coming over to kiss Jane on the cheek. "I can see that the two of you want to talk in private," he said understandingly. "I'll meet you tomorrow lunchtime, darling, and we'll go and choose your ring."

"Fine." Jane returned his kiss. "I had a lovely weekend. I'll write to your parents and thank them."

He grinned. "I think agreeing to marry me is thank you

enough. Until tomorrow. Good night, Lauri," he added almost gently.

She forced herself to smile. "Good night, Robin."

"Now," Jane said briskly once he had left. "Tell me what happened to upset you like this?"

In the past she had always found it easy to talk to Jane, but now she was too conscious of her own identity, feeling like an intruder, an interloper in the house that had been her home all her life. Besides, she could hardly tell Jane the truth. "Do I take it congratulations are in order?" she spoke of something quite different, Robin's remark too obvious for him to have meant anything else.

"Robin has asked me to marry him, yes," Jane blushed prettily.

"So you met his parents' approval?"

Jane flushed. "I know you don't think it important, but I happen to think it is. I remember the way my mother and father objected to some of my boyfriends when I was younger," she smiled in reminiscence.

"Did it stop you going out with them?" Lauri teased, glad that she had momentarily diverted her aunt's attention from the emotional state she was in.

"Usually the opposite," Jane admitted ruefully. "Although when they did approve that approval was hardly ever misplaced. In fact—" her voice hardened "—I think it only ever happened once."

"Do you think they would have approved of Robin?" Lauri asked curiously.

Jane seemed to give this some serious thought. "They would have liked him," she finally answered, "but not as a husband for me."

"But you're willing to risk it?"

"They were wrong once; they could be again."

Lauri didn't think they would be in Robin's case. But who was she to cast aspersions? Look at the man she herself had fallen in love with, someone completely unsuitable for her. "As long as you're happy, Jane."

"I think I will be. There's a lot more to love than sexual desire, fever-pitch excitement. It may not be quite what you have in mind for your life, but for me quiet security is just fine."

"Then once grandma and granddad were wrong?" Lauri probed gently.

"Yes." Jane looked down at her clenched hands. "But I don't even want to think about him," she said determinedly. "Not on the day I've agreed to marry Robin. You do like him, don't you?"

Well, she didn't *dis*like him. "It's what you feel for him that matters," she evaded.

"No," Jane frowned. "As you'll be living with us you have to like him, too."

Lauri looked startled. "Living with you? But I shall be staying here."

"So will we. Robin has agreed to move in here when we're married."

"Here?" Lauri looked even more startled. "But surely you'll want to be just the two of you. You'll be newly married; surely you won't want Steve and I underfoot?"

Her aunt looked firm. "I've brought you and Steve up since you were children."

"All the more reason—"

"It's all settled, Lauri. I only agreed to the marriage on condition that you would always have a home with us."

"But what if Robin hadn't agreed?" Lauri was aghast.

"Then I wouldn't have accepted his proposal. If Steve

would prefer that we didn't live here then we'll buy a house of our own, but whatever happens, you are going to live with us."

"Because I made a fool of myself over Alex Blair," Lauri said dully.

"Not at all," Jane denied sharply. "Because I love you, and I—I've always taken care of you." She gave a shaky smile. "Habits like that are hard to break."

"So I'm a habit now, am I?" she teased.

"A nice one," Jane smiled. "Now, what happened with Mr. Blair this weekend?"

"Not a lot," Lauri lied. Too much had happened for her to be able to take it all in. "But I'm not going to see him anymore. And I'm handing my notice in at Blair's."

"Isn't that a little drastic?"

She shook her head. "If I could I would make it impossible for him ever to find me again." Or the man who claimed to be her father!

"Well, at least make sure you have another job first," Jane advised.

"All right," she agreed, determined to hand in her notice the next day no matter what. Still only being on trial, she would only have to give a week's notice instead of the usual month. She might just manage to get through a week of possibly seeing Alex around every corner in the corridor. "Now, tell me, when's the engagement to be?"

Jane blushed. "Saturday. We're going to have a small dinner party here; just a few friends and relatives."

"Not Alex Blair, I hope," she said with a shudder.

"Until you started dating him I never considered he fitted into either of those categories. But Steve said something about Mr. Blair mentioning you and a wedding ring all in one breath."

"Only in jest. Besides, he knows I would never consider marrying him."

" *You* would never...." Jane spluttered with laughter. "My God, Lauri, he met his match in you. There have been any number of women the last few years who would gladly have become his wife."

"Well, for one thing he didn't ask me."

"And if he had?"

"Well, I— I told him I didn't want to get married."

"You told him...!"

Again Lauri blushed. "Well, the subject came up, just in passing, and so I told him I had no intention of ever getting married."

"And what was his answer to that, just in passing?" Jane said dryly.

Her mouth twisted derisively. "He said that once I had grown out of this childish ploy to be different that I would be in the marriage market like every other woman he knew."

"Cynical!"

"After working for him all this time I would have thought you would already have known that."

"I did, but it's nice to have your opinion confirmed. And the second thing?" Jane queried. "You did say, for one thing he hadn't asked you."

"Oh...oh, yes. Well, the second thing is that we aren't in love."

"Aren't you?"

"No!"

" *You* are."

"I hate him!"

"For the moment you do," Jane agreed gently, "because he's hurt you in some way. But once the hurt fades the love will return."

"Never! I don't love *him*."

"I know you, Lauri, so much better than you think I do. I fell in love at your age. I was hurt, too, and I denied that love until I almost believed it myself. But I don't think you ever get over your first real love."

"I'll get over Alex Blair," Lauri told her vehemently. "I'll make sure of it."

SHE DID HAND HER NOTICE IN the next day, much to the personnel officer's surprise. No doubt he had thought the Prescott family were here to stay.

Carly called her into her office midway through the morning. "Mr. Rand has told me you've handed in your notice." She came straight to the point. "I wondered whether it was because of anything I or one of the girls have done? I know they were being a bit bitchy last week about you dating Mr. Blair, but the majority of them seem to have forgotten it over the weekend."

She only wished she could do the same! "It has nothing to do with that, really. I just—"

"Oh, dear." Carly was looking at something over Lauri's shoulder. "Did you tell Mr. Blair you were leaving?"

She frowned. "No."

"Well, I think he's just found out," Carly grimaced.

"What do you— Oh!" she broke off as Alex burst into the room.

"Out." He held the door open for Carly to leave, which she did with no hesitation.

Lauri would have done the same in her position; Alex looked furious, his blue eyes blazing. But even so, he had no right to order Carly out of her own office—even if he did own it and the building it stood in. Lauri stood up, too, moving toward the door Alex had just slammed shut.

"Where the hell do you think you're going?" Alex rasped harshly.

Her head went back defiantly, her eyes challenging. "I'm going back to my desk to work. And if you don't like it you can sack me!"

"Rather a pointless exercise when you've already given in your notice," he retorted angrily.

"Exactly," she agreed sweetly. "Now, if you will let me pass?"

"Certainly." He moved aside, even opening the door for her.

To say Lauri was surprised by his acquiescence after storming down here was putting it mildly. But she managed to walk stiffly past him, not realizing he had followed her until she felt his familiar firm grasp on her upper arm as he marched her completely out of the office. Once outside he swung her round against the wall, his hands on either side of her head as he held her immovable. Not that she could have moved anyway, being much too aware of the male magnetism of him, the totally male smell of him as he held his body only inches away from her own.

"Where did you go yesterday?" he demanded to know.

"Go?" she repeated jerkily, cursing herself for being unnerved by him once again.

"When you walked out on Laurence."

She stiffened just at the mention of the man's name, in no way having come to terms with his relationship to her. "I went home," she said huskily.

"But not straight away," he persisted.

Her eyes flashed. "No, not straight away! I ... I went for a walk. I needed to think."

"And did you come to any conclusions?"

"Oh, yes," she said bitterly. "I came to the conclusion

that I'm justified in hating both you and your brother-in-law."

"Hate Laurence if you must, but don't include me in the emotion. What you feel toward me is far from hate."

"You flatter yourself," she scorned.

"Do I?" he asked huskily.

"Yes!"

"Let's see, shall we?" he murmured throatily before his dark head swooped and his mouth claimed hers, his body lowering fully onto hers, moving seductively against her as he determined to make her fully aware of him.

"Stop this!" She gasped for air as his mouth left hers to travel over her throat. "What if someone should see us?" She looked about them guiltily. "Alex, please."

"I might consider letting you go if you'll come up to my office with me."

"No!" she instantly refused.

"Then we stay here." He forced her mouth open again, wringing a response from her even while she fought him.

She relaxed against him, hoping to disconcert him, hardly able to control her elation as she heard him groan before taking her fully into his arms, his hands caressing her back. She let his caresses continue until she felt he was completely aroused by her, weakened by his own desire... and then she struck. She pushed him away as hard as she could, seeing by the glazed look in his eyes that he was still enmeshed in his passion for her, could even now not comprehend why she had left the possession of his arms.

She was almost drawn back against him by her own feelings for him, but she forced herself to walk away—more of a run, really—as she felt him collect his scattered wits and start to come after her. She turned to face him. "I think constant sexual advances from my employer are reason enough for me to wave my notice and leave right now."

Alex's eyes hardened. "Sexual advances? Why you little— I wasn't making sexual advances, I was—"

"Don't tell me," she scorned, "you were making love to me?"

"Yes!" he snapped, his face rigid.

Lauri gave a harsh laugh. "When you love someone it's called that, and I'm not stupid enough to think you love me. If you're hoping to persuade me to see Laurence, then you're wasting your time. I don't want to see him, just as I don't want to see you. I would have thought that was obvious by now, or are you just too conceited to have got the message?"

"Oh, I've got the message, once and for all. You're a stupid, stubborn female, and I don't know why I've wasted my time on you this long. Run away, little girl. It's the last time you'll need to do so on my account. I'm tired of playing little girl games. I'm going out to get myself a woman, and right now."

Each word was like a blow to Lauri, a physical blow. She gave a choked sob before turning on her heel and running.

THE PARTY WAS GOING WELL, all the work and preparation beforehand now seeming worth it. The engagement hadn't been announced yet, and wouldn't be for some hours, not until everyone was here.

Lauri was responsible for the arrangement of the room, the fine selection of records and the beautiful display of food. She had had all week to organize this party, to make it a special occasion for Jane and Robin. There had been nothing else for her to do; she hadn't managed to secure another job for herself yet.

It seemed poor Jane had been bearing the brunt of Alex's anger all week. His attitude seemed to be that if he couldn't get at Lauri, then her aunt would do instead. Poor Jane had been made to work late every evening, making Robin furious.

Lauri had seen nothing of Alex herself. Not that she had expected to after their last stormy encounter. But she had longed to, had wanted him with a fever that made her pride seem stupid and childish. But if she were to go to him and he were to reject her, as he was likely to do, she would be more hurt than ever.

She had given Laurence Daniels a lot of thought, too. No matter how much she hated the thought of discovering he was her father, she was also drawn to him, to getting to know the man he was.

She went once again to answer the doorbell, sure that almost everyone was here now. Her eyes widened as she saw Alex Blair standing on the doorstep. She had wanted so much to see him, and now that he was here in front of her she could only stand and gape at him.

"What's going on?" he quirked an eyebrow at the sound of music and chatter coming from the room behind her.

She swallowed hard, unable to take her eyes off him, off how attractive he looked in cream, fitted trousers and a cream silk shirt that made his tanned skin all the more noticeable. "A...a party," she answered haltingly.

He nodded. "Can you leave it?"

"Leave?"

"Laurence needs you. I told him I would come and get you. Don't worry," he added grimly. "I'm not here on my own account. I've given up on children."

"And found yourself a woman," she said with remembered bitterness.

"Yes."

"I hope she proves satisfactory."

"Very. Now, will you come to the hospital with me or not?"

"Is he worse?" She couldn't keep the concern out of her voice.

"The doctors are worried about him."

"And so are you, apparently."

He shrugged. "Let's just say that now I'm a man I've decided to put such childish things as revenge behind me." He gave her a pointed look. "Something some people can talk about but never put into practice. Hating Laurence was juvenile and destructive. Who's to say I wouldn't do the same thing, trapped in a marriage that hadn't had any love in it for years? Laurence suffered for trying to find love; by loving your mother I think he was punished enough."

"But his loving my mother produced me," Lauri said dully.

"He wants to see you, Lauren." He studied her closely. "And I think deep down you really want to see him."

"Yes," she admitted with a sigh. "I want—I want to know about the love they shared, how he felt when he saw me for the first time. There are so many things I want to know. Alex, I—"

"Lauri, are you— Mr. Blair!" Steve stood behind them. "What are you doing here?" he asked bluntly.

"Borrowing your niece for an hour or so," Alex answered him pleasantly enough.

Steve looked at Lauri. "But you can't leave now. What about the engagement?"

Alex stiffened, looking at her sharply. "What engagement?"

"Jane's," she supplied. "She and Robin are getting engaged tonight; that's what this party is about."

"I see. Well, I'll only keep Lauren an hour," he told Steve. "We...we have some things to discuss."

"Jane will be very disappointed if you aren't here," Steve warned her.

"I'll be here," she called as Alex literally dragged her away.

"So mummy and daddy approved of her," Alex drawled on the way to the hospital.

Having met Mr. and Mrs. Harley tonight, Lauri didn't envy Jane her future parents-in-law. They were both too much like Robin, with no sense of humor or fun, and Mr. Harley was terribly henpecked by his wife. "There's no need to sneer," she snapped, indignant for her aunt. "Jane thought it important."

"And I don't. We'll have to agree to differ."

"We usually do—differ, I mean," she answered absently, most of her thoughts with the man lying sick in a hospital bed, the man she had recently discovered was her father.

"Not all the time," Alex said huskily. "I can remember a few occasions when we both wanted the same thing."

"I'm trying to forget them," she said curtly, knowing she would never be able to erase the memory from her mind of being in his arms. "You said Laurence was worse." She changed the subject.

"I said he wanted to see you," he corrected.

Lauri turned to give him an accusing look. "So he isn't worse."

"He's still a very ill man."

"But no worse."

"No worse," he confirmed coolly. "In fact, a little better."

"Then why—"

"But not well enough," he cut in on her heated query, "to be able to come after you, which is what he has been wanting to do all week."

"He has?" she asked uncertainly.

"You're his daughter; he loves you."

"He doesn't even know me," she scorned.

"Maybe not, but I do, and I've told him all about you."

"All?" she blushed.

Alex grinned. "Well, perhaps not all. Some things are too private to tell a third person, especially if he happens to be your father."

Laurence Daniels looked so pleased to see her she felt guilty about her desertion of him earlier in the week.

"You came," he said dazedly. "Alex said he would get you here, but I didn't believe him. Knowing Alex as I do I should have realized he would succeed."

Lauri was amazed at how much better he looked, a more healthy pink to his cheeks, a little more flesh on his bones, although his eyes remained sunken and ill looking. But her animosity toward him wasn't completely forgotten, her reply to him sharp. "Alex was as unscrupulous in getting me here as he is in all of his other dealings." She glared at the subject of their conversation, meeting only amusement in those steady blue eyes. "And if I'm not back for the announcement of my aunt's engagement, I'll personally throttle him."

Laurence frowned. "Your aunt?"

She gave him a concerned glance. "Yes. Jane is getting engaged tonight, and—"

"Jane!" he repeated in a strangulated voice. "You have an aunt called Jane?"

"Why, yes." She frowned her puzzlement.

"But Jane isn't your aunt, she . . . she's your *mother*!"

CHAPTER TEN

LAURI FELT STRONG ARMS go about her as she swayed, guiding her over to a chair as she turned to stare at the man in the bed propped up by numerous pillows.

"Hell, Laurence," Alex turned on him angrily. "You can't go throwing accusations like that about. Look at her; you've shocked the life out of her."

"But I— Jane is the woman I love, the woman I've always loved," Laurence told them dazedly. "She's the mother of my child."

"*My* mother?" Lauri was just as dazed.

"Yes," he nodded.

"Thank God for that!" she sighed raggedly, feeling only relief at his disclosure. It may be even more of a shock than finding out he was her father, but at least it meant the woman she had always believed to be her mother had never been unfaithful to her husband. And in truth Jane had always been more of a mother to her than anyone else had.

"You're all right?" Alex asked her gently.

"Yes," she nodded.

He turned to his brother-in-law. "Perhaps you wouldn't mind explaining," he said tersely.

"I— Just tell me one thing, Lauri," Laurence pleaded. "Jane, my Jane, is still alive?"

She gave a shaky smile. "She's brought me up since I was a child."

"My God!" he groaned, collapsing weakly back onto the pillows. "I can hardly believe it."

"I'm not sure I can, either," Lauri choked.

"Explain, Laurence," Alex commanded, sitting beside Lauri to take her hand in his, his thumb rhythmically caressing the delicate veins at her wrist.

She felt grateful for his hold on her, feeling somehow as if all sanity had deserted her. It now appeared that far from being the orphan she had believed herself to be the last ten years, that both her mother and father were still alive. Why had Jane, her mother, never told her the truth? Was she ashamed of her, wanting to shield their true relationship? It somehow didn't fit in with the Jane she knew.

"Jane was only seventeen when I met her," Laurence began talking, "while I was already thirty-five." His look was distant, as if he were reliving it all. "I loved her on sight. We met quite accidentally in the park. She was beautiful, had a startling honesty that almost frightened me, a zest for life that I craved. I began to take her out, quite innocent little outings at first, because I knew she only saw me as a friend. I suppose she considered me too old for any romantic involvement," he added ruefully. "But gradually I felt her feelings for me begin to change, knew that she was coming to care for me in the same way I cared for her."

"And I'm sure you omitted to tell her you were already married," Alex put in dryly.

Laurence flushed. "How did you know that?"

"After having her as my secretary for three years I believe I know a little about Jane. She would never have had anything to do with you if she had known about Beth."

"You're right, of course," Laurence said dully. "But I loved her too much to lose her. So I kept quiet about Beth, which in the end was my downfall. Jane found out and re-

fused to see me again. When I went round to her parents'
house they told me she had gone away to stay with relatives.
They refused to tell me where. I...I thought I would die
without her."

"You had no idea she had gone away because she was
expecting your child?" Alex prompted.

"None at all. It only happened the once, you see." An
embarrassed hue colored his cheeks. "It never occurred to
me.... Beth was in hospital for a week having tests, tests to
see if there was anything to be done for her." He put up a
hand to his temples. "I'm sorry about this, Alex, I know
she was your sister, but.... There had been so many tests,
so many disappointments, and each time Beth's hatred of
me got worse. I think Jane must have sensed some of my
despair because when I—when we— She gave herself to me
with no reservations."

"That would be Jane," Alex said coldly. "You took advantage of the fact that she loved you, that she knew nothing of your loveless, sterile marriage, and you ruined her
life for her."

"Yes," Laurence choked, "it seems I did all of that. But
until I saw Lauri just over a week ago I had no idea of just
how much damage I had done her. And then Lauri told me
her mother was dead! God, I wanted to die, too. When Beth
died and I decided to come back to England I had some
crazy idea of finding Jane again, although how I intended
doing that I have no idea. And then Alex turned up at the
airport with you! I knew straight away who you were, and I
thought Alex had done it deliberately to hurt me."

"And instead I was as shocked as you were," Alex told
him harshly. "More so probably," he added bitterly.

"Not really, Alex," Lauri spoke for the first time, challenge in her voice. "Through me you thought you would get

the revenge on Laurence that you've always wanted. You decided to make love to me, get me to admit to loving you in the heat of your experienced caresses, and then taunt him with the knowledge that you had his daughter exactly where you wanted her, in your arms and in your bed."

"Lauri!" Laurence was shocked. "You're wrong about that."

"Am I?" she asked Alex shrilly. "Well, am I?" she demanded.

His eyes were like an icy blue ocean, cold and forbidding. He shrugged. "Maybe not so far wrong."

"You see," she said bitterly, whatever hope she had had left crumbling at her feet. "But it didn't work."

"We were interrupted during my seduction of her," Alex informed the older man carelessly.

Laurence's eyes widened. "Alex, it isn't true. You told me—"

"The first part of it is true," Alex admitted cruelly. "I'm not sure I would have cared a damn about revenge on you if I had managed to get Lauren into bed."

"I hate you!" she told him vehemently.

He shrugged at Laurence. "As you can see, my plan failed."

Laurence frowned. "Alex? I thought you said—"

"Forget what I said," he dismissed. "Lauren's version is so much better than mine, don't you think—so much neater."

"No, I don't," Laurence snapped.

"Well, it's the one we'll all have to settle for right now," Alex told him abruptly. "There's something else of more importance to deal with at the moment. Are you aware of the fact that your beloved Jane is even now on the point of becoming engaged to another man."

"Because she was once hurt so badly that the only thing she requires from a husband is that he be safe and reliable and will never let her down," Lauri informed them coldly.

Laurence's eyes darkened with pain. "Is that what she said?"

"Yes," she answered cruelly.

He drew a ragged breath. "God, I must have almost destroyed her."

"We have to concern ourselves with the present," Alex told him firmly. "If nothing else the two of you owe it to each other to meet...and preferably before the engagement takes place."

Lauri gave him a hard stare. "You don't expect Jane— my mother," she amended shakily, "you don't expect her to still love him?"

"None of us can know how she feels," he snapped. "That's why we have to get her here. Laurence is hardly in any condition to go to her. I'll go and get her."

Lauri gave a scornful smile. "You may have got me here on a pretext, but I doubt Jane will be so easily persuaded to leave her own engagement party."

"We'll see, shall we?" he taunted.

"We certainly will," she said smugly.

"I shouldn't be long, Laurence," he assured the other man, standing up and in consequence letting Lauri's hand drop to her side. "Don't worry, she'll be here."

"Huh," Lauri scoffed.

His narrowed blue eyes leveled on her. "As for you, young lady, while I'm prepared to overlook...certain things you do and say, when all this is over you and I have a few things to discuss."

"I can't think of a single thing we have to talk about."

He smiled. "Maybe not, but I can. So be warned."

She turned away. "You can't force me to even ac-knowledge your existence."

"Oh, I can force you to acknowledge a damn sight more than that...any time I choose to. I just don't choose to just yet. I shouldn't be long, Laurence," he added deter-minedly.

"She won't come with him," Lauri said obstinately once she was alone with Laurence Daniels. "Why should she?"

"Because I still love her."

"You don't know her!" Her eyes sparkled angrily. "You haven't seen her for almost eighteen years. You don't know the woman she has become."

"I can see how well she's brought you up, what a beauti-ful young woman she's made of you. You're everything she was at that age—loyal, trusting and independent."

"But she's never told me she's my mother! Doesn't that tell you anything? She's ashamed of my birth, of having once loved you. She's had years to tell me the truth, and yet she chose not to. I think the reason for that is obvious."

"I hope you're wrong," he said fervently. "I really hope you're wrong."

Lauri didn't know what she wanted anymore. To find that *Jane* was the woman Laurence Daniels loved. And Jane must have still loved him after her baby had been born. Why else would she have called her daughter Lauren, a female name as much like Laurence as she could make it?

She wasn't surprised when Alex came back into the hos-pital room alone, although his first words soon disillusioned her.

"Jane's outside," he informed them almost trium-phantly. "She wants to see you, Lauren."

She stood up, swallowing nervously. This would be the first time she had ever faced Jane as her daughter. She

tepped outside the room, conscious of Alex standing be-
ind her. As she looked at Jane her whole world suddenly
oomed back into focus. Jane loved her, had always loved
er, and their relationship had always been much closer
han just aunt and niece—she knew that now.

Jane rushed toward her, her anxiety evident. "Are you
ll right?" she demanded to know. "Mr. Blair would only
ell me that you were at the hospital." She searched Lauri's
ace for sign of injury. "What happened?"

"I'm not hurt," Lauri assured her with a smile, tears
hining in her eyes. "I'm not hurt at all ... mum."

Jane's face went very white. "M-mum?" she gasped, her
ace now a sickly gray color.

"Yes." Lauri squeezed her hand reassuringly. "And
here's someone in that room over there who would like
ery much to talk to you."

"Wh-who is it?" she gasped.

"Can't you guess?" Lauri teased.

"La-Laurence?" Jane asked dazedly.

Lauri nodded. "My father. He's Alex's brother-in-law."

Jane looked at her employer. "Then Beth—"

"Was my sister," he acknowledged gently. "But that's all
n the past. Laurence is all alone in the world now."

"He loves us both very much," Lauri continued, "and
e wants the chance to prove it. I'd like you to give him that
hance," she added softly.

Jane's big brown eyes flooded with tears, her usual calm
ssurance completely deserting her. "You ... you like him?"

"Very much. Much more than I do Robin," she added
nischievously.

"Oh, my God—Robin!" Jane turned to Alex. "I com-
letely forgot about him when you said Lauri was at the
ospital. Whatever must he think of me?"

"It's all right," Alex soothed her. "I had a word with Steve while you were getting your coat. He was going to take Robin aside and explain the situation to him." He looked at his wristwatch. "The party should be breaking up about now."

"Oh, this is terrible!" Jane put her hands up to her face. "He's going to hate me when he knows the truth."

"Does that really matter?" Lauri asked gently. "If I had known before that I was your daughter, with Robin as my prospective future stepfather, I would have told you exactly what I think of him. I hate him. He's stuffy and disapproving, and he would never have made you truly happy."

"So you don't want me to marry him?"

"I'd rather have my real father. I'll even be a bridesmaid at the wedding," she smiled shakily.

Jane put up a hand to her tousled hair. "Laurence really wants to see me, after all this time?"

"He's never stopped loving you." Lauri pushed her in the direction of Laurence's room. "Now go on—mum. That might take a bit of time to get used to," she laughed. "But I'll get the hang of it."

Jane looked at her anxiously. "You don't have to, you know. I don't deserve—"

"I want to," Lauri told her firmly. "Unless you would rather I didn't?"

"I'd like it," Jane admitted shyly. "All this time I've had to pretend the casual relationship of an aunt, to actually have you as my daughter will be... breathtaking."

"Why did you— No." Lauri shook her head. "It doesn't matter. We can talk later, when you've spoken to Lau—my father." She couldn't quite bring herself to call him dad, although she thought that, too, might come in time.

"I know what you were going to ask," Jane said dully.

"And I'd like to answer you now, before I speak to Laurence. I want you to try and understand, both of you, that I was very young, and...and pregnant by a man I felt had betrayed me in the worst way possible. My parents were wonderful; they stood by me all during my pregnancy, and when you were born they loved you as much as I did. But 'm jumping ahead slightly, missing out the most important part. When we realized Laurence wasn't going to leave me alone, I went to stay with my brother and his wife. Robert and Adelle had been married for years, but they couldn't have a family of their own."

Lauri gasped. "Was that why—"

"No, I didn't give you away to them," her mother told her firmly. "When I brought you home, to their home, I could see Adelle was more interested in you than she should have been, but at the time I saw no harm in it. Then my parents were killed. It was as if my prop had been taken out from under me. I fell apart completely. I had a nervous breakdown. The authorities agreed that Robert and Adelle should look after you until I was well enough to. It was almost eighteen months later before I felt able to cope with being a mother without a supportive husband. By that time it was too late; you had already accepted Robert and Adelle as your parents—you even called them mummy and daddy. They were wrong to let that happen, but I think they longed for a child of their own so much that they didn't think they were doing any harm. I had no choice but to become your aunt, although I always intended you to know the truth one day."

"Why not when they died?" Lauri asked huskily.

"You had idolized Robert as your father," Jane sighed. "I just couldn't do that to you when you had just lost him. After that there just never seemed to be a right time. Maybe I was

being a coward again, I don't know, but I kept to my role o
loving aunt, longing to tell you the truth but knowing I'd lef
it much too late."

"You haven't." Lauri squeezed her hand. "Not for Lau
rence or me. You do still love him, don't you?"

"I never stopped. But he was married, with no chance o
a divorce, and I knew I had to give him up or feel guilty fo
the rest of my life. I never meant to hurt your sister, Alex."
She looked at him pleadingly.

"I know that," he said gently. "Now don't you think yo
should go in and see Laurence? Unless you want him t
suffer another heart attack...."

Jane frowned worriedly. "Is that why he's here?"

"Yes." Alex smiled. "So would I be if suddenly faced
with a daughter of eighteen."

"Anything's possible," Lauri put in bitterly.

He gave her an angry look. "Laurence is very eager t
see you," he spoke to Jane. "Lauri and I will be in th
visitors' room when you're ready to leave."

"Thank you." She gave a nervous smile before goin
into Laurence's room.

"I thought you handled that very well." Alex sat oppo
site her, shielding her from the other people in the room.

"Am I supposed to thank you for your praise?" sh
asked sarcastically.

"No," he sighed. "I don't expect you to do anything."

"Good." Her sparkling eyes glared her hatred of him
"Because accepting Laurence as my father and Jane as m
mother doesn't mean I go one step further and accept yo
as my lover."

"I didn't ask," he said harshly. "Your attitude toward you
parents may have been totally adult, but you're still th
child I don't want in my life. So before refusing to share m

bed, wait until you're asked. Get it?" he asked vehemently.

"Yes," she acknowledged huskily.

THE WEDDING TOOK PLACE three months later—a very quiet affair because of Laurence's recent ill health. Lauri had got to know her father well during the last few months, had come to like and respect him, although she still had a little trouble calling him dad. That he and Jane adored each other there could be no doubt. It was as if their years apart had never been, and Lauri had never seen Jane so animated.

Steve still seemed to be rather dazed by the sudden turn of events, although being the one to tell Robin to get lost had more than made up for that. Not that he had been that blunt, but Robin and his parents had made a hasty retreat when informed of his fiancée's other family.

Much to Lauri's annoyance, Alex Blair had been chosen as best man, and etiquette decreed that as the bridesmaid she be accompanied by him. Steve brought along his girl friend of two months, and the six of them had dinner at one of the exclusive restaurants in town before splitting up into pairs and going their separate ways.

Not that Lauri wanted to be with Alex Blair, but in the circumstances she had little choice. Jane and Laurence had gone to a hotel for the night, Steve and Joanna had gone on to an all-night party, and so she was left with no choice but to accept Alex's offer of a lift home.

"It seems strange to think I once said Jane had no hidden depths," he remarked with amusement, the windscreen wipers on as the rain pelted down on the car. "She certainly kept you hidden."

"I would probably have done the same in her position," Lauri bristled angrily.

"No, you wouldn't." Alex shook his head firmly. "For

all her confidence and air of self-assurance, you have more strength of character than Jane. You wouldn't have collapsed, either mentally or physically, as she did. You're a fighter. You've done nothing but fight me since the moment we met."

She raised her eyebrows. "A question of self-preservation."

"Explain that remark," he ordered curtly.

"You've made no secret of your physical attraction toward me, although why it should exist I have no idea—"

"I have." His gaze ran over her appraisingly. "Oh, yes, I have."

Lauri gave him a surprised glance. "I thought you said you were no longer interested."

"Until you grew up. I happen to think you have. But we're diverting. Carry on with your explanation."

Her mouth tightened. "You're so bossy. I have no idea why I still—"

"Yes?" he prompted as she bit her lip.

"Nothing." She blushed. "As you said, we're diverting."

"But such interesting diversions," he grinned. "I believe you were about to say you were still attracted to me, too."

No such thing! She had been about to admit her *love* for him. She remembered how Jane—her mother—had told her that Laurence was her first love, and how he had remained the only love of her life, that he was now her last love, too. Alex meant the same thing to Lauri—her first love and her last love. "We were talking about my self-preservation," she reminded firmly.

"Okay," he sighed.

"Right. Well, you told me at the beginning that to you familiarity always leads to boredom."

"I believe the word I used was 'contempt.' And I feel far from contempt for you."

She looked away from the warmth in his eyes. "Yes, well, you made no attempt to pretend your going out with me at all was anything but a way of becoming unattracted to me. You even *made* me admit to being attracted to you."

"And how did I do that?" They had come to a stop outside her house, the car engine off, only the sound of the heavy rain to disturb them.

She blushed. "You know how."

"Like this?" He bent forward to claim her softly parted lips, tasting their sweetness with slow enjoyment. "And this?" He invaded her inner warmth with the sensuous tip of his tongue, his hand moving caressingly down her throat to cup her breast.

The air was electric between them, Lauri's body trembling with the desire she had been denied for so long. And she was melting, melting, becoming part of Alex through sheer force of will on his part.

"This car wasn't designed for making love," he murmured throatily, his lips traveling over the creamy skin his exploring hands had revealed, working a slow erotic pattern to the rosy peak of her breast, holding her tightly against him at her cry of pleasure.

She swallowed hard. "Making love?" she questioned his description, as she had done once before.

"Yes, damn you!" He looked up at her with deep blue eyes. "Making love!"

"Alex...?"

"I love you, you stupid child," he rasped angrily.

Shock warred with anger. "Alex, you can't tell a girl you love her in that fashion," she admonished, laughter finally winning.

"I just did. But if it makes you any happier...." His hands came up to cup each side of her face, and he took his time kissing each delicious feature, finally moving back to look at her as if he wanted never to see anything but her face. "I know I've been a brute to you at times, darling Lauren, but I took one look at those flashing green eyes, freckled snub nose and adorable, kissable mouth—" his actions suited his words "—and I knew I'd met the girl I was going to marry."

"You certainly didn't act like it," she complained, still not able to believe what he was saying to her.

"I know that, because 'girl' was the appropriate word. I'm used to sophisticates, women of my own age who wanted what I wanted."

"And I didn't?" she asked shyly.

"Not at first. It took all of my persuasion to get you to even go out with me." He frowned. "Lauren, do you love me?"

"You haven't finished telling me everything yet," she stubbornly refused to answer him.

"You little— Okay," he sighed, touching her lips with the tip of his thumb. "God, I want to kiss you!"

"Later," she dismissed impatiently.

"You really mean that?"

"Yes! Now, please...."

He drew a ragged breath. "When you say yes like that— All right, I'll finish what I was saying. But later—" His eyes were eloquent with meaning. "I loved you on sight. But I knew I was in for trouble because the next time I saw you you were kissing that boy in the lift," he said with remembered anger.

"He was kissing me," she corrected. "And I soon forgot about that when you kissed me immediately afterward."

"You did?"

"Mmm," she nodded.

"I wish I'd known, I was furious—"

"I gathered that."

"So would you have been if you had been me. After that I used any way I could of seeing you—blackmail, seduction, you name it and I tried it. But I never saw you as a means to revenge on Laurence. Never! But I was going about winning you in completely the wrong way. Like I said, you're a fighter, and by forcing you into seeing me I was ruining my chances."

"I was very attracted to you."

"Was?" His fingers bit into her arm.

"Still am," she corrected.

"Have you heard enough now?" he groaned, his gaze locked hungrily on her mouth.

"No."

"God, you're a little tease! It would be difficult to make love to you in the front seat of this car, but I think I might manage it," he warned. "Through sheer desperation."

"You should have brought the Rolls," she said practically. "There would have been more room in that. Actually, the simplest thing to do would be to go into the house; we have it all to ourselves."

"Lauren?" He looked hopeful.

"Mmm?" she asked innocently.

"I'm warning you—"

"Oh, I love it when you come on all strong and domineering." She gave him a mischievous glance from beneath lowered lashes.

"Will you be serious for five minutes?" he snapped tautly. "I never thought that when I proposed my intended bride would laugh at me!"

"I'm not laughing, Alex. And you haven't proposed."

"I haven't?" he frowned. "No, I haven't, have I? And I

don't intend to," he said with the old forcefulness. "You're going to marry me...and no arguments. I have your parents' permission, and that's all that matters."

"You've spoken to my mother and father?" Her eyes widened.

"Yes, I've spoken to them, but Laurence knew how I felt the day we met him at the airport. That's why he knew it wasn't true when you accused me of wanting you only for revenge on him."

"Then he's known more than I have," she said with remembered pain. "That day at the airport you were horrible to me. You even said you were going to see Connie Mears."

"Pure fabrication, as was the woman I told you I had found. I don't want anyone but you; I haven't since the moment we met. A little self-preservation on *my* part, I'm afraid. God, you can't imagine the shock I had when I realized you were Laurence's daughter. I think I must have gone mad for a few days. I just wanted to hurt you."

"That night you took me to your apartment," she said huskily.

"Yes," Alex agreed heavily. "I also realized that night that I had to marry you. When I hurt you so badly I realized just how much I loved you, that by hurting you I was just hurting myself. I followed you back to your home with the intention of asking you to marry me. But Steve interrupted, and after that there never seemed to be a right time. Laurence collapsed, and I was worried that he was going to die before you even knew he was your father."

She smoothed his brow. "We've done nothing but hurt each other."

"But no more. I love you, Lauren. You're the most important thing in the world to me. I just can't live without you. Now tell me you love me, or must I use force?"

Knowing what direction his force would take, she willingly opted for the latter.

"Do you love me?" he demanded before he would even kiss her.

"Very much," she nodded.

"Then tell me!"

"You said you didn't want a ring through your nose," she reminded him teasingly. "Or a collar and lead around your throat."

"And you told me you didn't want to get married."

She smiled. "I lied."

"Tell me!" he groaned.

"I love you very, very much," she said huskily. "And if you don't soon kiss me I think I'll die."

"You're going to make a shameless wife," he chuckled. "Thank God!"

She raised her eyebrows. "I haven't said I'll marry you."

"No." He claimed her mouth in a savagely arousing kiss. "But you will."

And she did.